# CHEMISTRY
*first*

# CHEMISTRY *first*

George Bethell

David Coppock

OXFORD

UNIVERSITY PRESS

# OXFORD
UNIVERSITY PRESS

Great Clarendon Street, Oxford OX2 6DP

Oxford University Press is a department of the University of Oxford.
It furthers the University's objective of excellence in research, scholarship,
and education by publishing worldwide in

Oxford New York

Auckland Cape Town Dar es Salaam Hong Kong Karachi
Kuala Lumpur Madrid Melbourne Mexico City Nairobi
New Delhi Shanghai Taipei Toronto

With offices in

Argentina Austria Brazil Chile Czech Republic France Greece
Guatemala Hungary Italy Japan Poland Portugal Singapore
South Korea Switzerland Thailand Turkey Ukraine Vietnam

Oxford is a registered trade mark of Oxford University Press
in the UK and in certain other countries

© George Bethell and David Coppock 1999

The moral rights of the authors have been asserted

Database right Oxford Unviersity Press (maker)

First published 1999

British Library Cataloguing in Publication Data

Data available

ISBN: 978 0 19 914732 8

20 19 18 17 16 15 14

Typeset by Ian Foulis and Associates, Plymouth, Devon
Printed in Singapore by KHL Printing Co Pte Ltd

# Acknowledgements

The publishers would like to thank the following for providing
photographs:

8 (left) SPL/ Sindo Farina, 8 (top right) SPL/ Ed Young, 8 (bottom right)
FLPA/ P. Reynolds, 9 (left) SPL/ Adam Hart-Davis, 9 (right) FLPA/
Silvestris, 10 (top left) OUP library, 10 (top centre) Peter Gould, 10 (top
right) OUP library, 10 (bottom left) SPL/ Dr George Gornacz, 10 (bottom
right) Peter Gould, 12 SPL/ Martin Dohrn, 14 (top) Peter Gould, 14
(centre) Scotch Whisky Association, 14 (bottom) Hutchison Library, 16
(top) OUP library, 16 (bottom) SPL/ Mark Burnett, 18 (top left) FLPA/
Dembinsky, 18 (top right) Peter Gould, 18 (centre left) OUP library, 18
(centre right) Peter Gould, 18 (bottom left) OUP library, 19 (top left) OUP
library, 19 (top centre) SPL/ Martyn F. Chillmaid, 19 (top right) OUP
library, 19 (bottom right) Stock Market/ Craig Hammell, 25 Chris
Honeywell, 26 (top) Mary Evans Picture Library, 26 (bottom) Topham
Picture Source, 27 (top) Chris Honeywell, 27 (bottom) Chris Honeywell,
29 Hulton Getty, 30 Zefa, 31 (left) SPL/ Damien Lovegrove, 31 (centre)
Barnabys Picture Library/ R. F. W. Cramp, 31 (right) SPL/ Magrath
Photography, 32 Chris Honeywell, 34 OUP library, 37 (top left)
Hutchison Library, 37 (centre left) SPL/ Martin Bond, 37 (bottom left)
SPL/ Richard Folwell, 37 (top right) SPL/ Rosenfeld Images, 38 OSF/ G. I.
Bernard, 40 (left) Dr Terry Jennings, 40 (centre left) Zefa, 40 (centre right)
Argos, 40 (right) Chris Honeywell, 41 British Steel, 45 (bottom left) OUP
library, 45 (centre left) Zefa, 45 (top right) Hutchison Library, 45 (bottom
right) British Airways, 46 (top) FLPA/ Gerard Lacz, 46 (bottom) Heinz, 47
(top) Peter Gould, 47 (bottom) OUP library, 48 (top) OUP library, 48
(bottom) Zefa, 49 (top) Zefa, 49 (centre) Zefa, 49 (bottom) British Gas, 51
OUP library, 52 Chris Honeywell, 54 (top) Building Research
Establishment, 54 (bottom) OUP library, 55 OUP library, 56 OUP
library, 57 Zefa, 59 (left) Pilkington Glass, 59 (right) SPL/ James
Stevenson, 60 (top) Zefa, 60 (bottom) Allsport/ Bob Martin, 61 (top left)
RSPB/ Michael W. Richards, 61 (bottom left) OSF/ Kathie Atkinson, 61
(bottom right) OSF/ Mike Birkhead, 62 (top) SPL/ Vanessa Vick, 62
(centre) Zefa, 62 (bottom) Zefa, 63 (top) Mercedes–Benz, 63 (centre) Labatt
Brewing UK, 63 (bottom) The Rover Group, 64 Chris Honeywell, 65 (left)
Shell, 65 (top right) Zefa, 65 (top centre) SPL/ Martin Bond, 65 (bottom
right) Chris Honeywell, 66 (top left) SPL/ Bruce Iverson, 66 (bottom left)
SPL/ Tek Image, 66 (top right) OUP library, 70 (top) FLPA/ M. B.
Withers, 70 (bottom) OUP library, 71 (top) Tilcon, 71 (bottom) FLPA/
Derek Hall, 72 Thermit Welding, 73 (left) OUP library, 73 (right) Peter
Gould, 74 OUP library, 75 (top) TRH/ Vickers, 75 (bottom) OSF/ John
McCammon, 77 (top) Bruce Coleman/ L. C. Marigo, 77 (bottom) Bruce
Coleman/ Norman Myers, 78 Electrolux, 79 (top left) SPL/ Malcolm
Fielding, 79 (bottom left) OUP library, 79 (right) Synetix, 80 (top left)
Peter Gould, 80 (top right) SPL/ Simon Fraser, 80 (bottom right) OUP
library, 85 (top) OUP library, 85 (bottom) OUP library, 86 (top left) Chris
Honeywell, 86 (top right) OUP library, 86 (bottom right) SPL/ Will
McIntyre, 88 Chris Honeywell, 90 (top) Chris Honeywell, 90 (centre)
Chris Honeywell, 90 (bottom) Chris Honeywell, 91 Chris Honeywell, 92
OUP library, 93 (top) Bruce Coleman/ Eric Crichton, 93 (bottom) Holt
Studios, 94 Chris Honeywell, 95 (top) Zefa, 95 (bottom) SPL/ Dr Jeremy
Burgess, 97 OUP library, 98 ICI/ OUP library, 100 (top left) FLPA/ R.
Tidman, 100 (top centre) FLPA/ Mark Newman, 100 (top right) FLPA/
Maurice Nimmo, 100 (bottom right) Geoscience Features, 101 (left)
Natural History Museum/ Martin Poulsford, 101 (right) Peter Gould, 102
(top) OUP library, 102 (bottom) Geoscience Features, 103 (right) SPL/
Simon Fraser, 103 (left) SPL/ Alfred Pasieka, 104 (top) Aspect Picture
Library, 104 (bottom) Picturepoint, 107 Zefa, 108 (left) Rex Features, 108
(right) FLPA/ R. Tidman.

The artwork is by: Brian Beckett, Elitta Fell, Ian Foulis Associates, David La
Grange, Nick Hawken, Oxford Illustrators, Jones Sewell, Alan Rowe, Julie
Tolliday, and Galina Zolfaghari.

# Introduction

Chemistry is the study of all the substances that make up the physical world around us. It covers the physical properties and the reactions of all the elements and compounds we find both here on Earth and throughout the universe. This not only makes chemistry an exciting subject but also leads to very practical applications. As you will see, new materials and fuels from the petrochemical industry, fertilizers from the agrochemical industry, and medicines from the pharmaceutical industry are just some of the things that chemists develop to improve the world in which we live. Of course, we face problems such as corrosion and pollution, but knowledge of chemistry can help us to tackle these.

This book has been written for students, like you, studying chemistry in secondary schools. It covers all the chemical processes that you need for Key Stage 3 of the National Curriculum. However, in many places it goes into much greater depth, helping you to develop the kind of understanding needed to gain the highest grades in your SATs. It will also provide a very solid foundation if you are preparing for GCSE.

There are six main chapters covering many important topics, particularly those that affect us in our everyday lives. There is even a chapter on the geology of the Earth. You may find that this overlaps with things you have met in your physics book. This is because the geological changes on our planet are due to both chemical reactions and physical forces.

The book sets out each topic over two or four pages and there are lots of diagrams and photographs to help you. There are also questions and activities to check that you have understood the main ideas. Each chapter finishes with a page of questions to help you test your knowledge and to prepare for examinations. Of course, chemistry is more than just learning from books, however good they are, and your school's programme of practical work will help you to develop important experimental skills.

To get the most out of this book:

- use the contents page to find out where the major topics are covered;
- use the index to find the pages where you can read about particular key words;
- use the questions within a chapter to test your knowledge as you go;
- carry out the activities suggested to reinforce your understanding;
- use the questions at the end of each chapter to prepare for tests and examinations.

We hope that you will enjoy using this book and finish it feeling confident that you can use the ideas and methods of chemistry to understand the way our world works.

George Bethell

David Coppock

# Contents

# 1 What is chemistry?

*What is chemistry?*
*What do chemists do?*
*Is chemistry dangerous?*
*How can we use our knowledge of chemistry?*

Chemistry is the study of materials. Chemists study the physical properties of substances. They are also interested in the **reactions** between different chemicals. This involves them in making scientific hypotheses about what will happen when substances are mixed, and then carefully observing and measuring any changes that take place. Chemists draw conclusions from the results of their experiments.

Some chemical reactions can be violent and others produce poisonous substances. It is always important to follow safety instructions when doing chemistry experiments.

*Chemists try to understand chemical reactions through experimentation, observation and measurement.*

Understanding chemistry helps industry to make good use of the materials around us. For example, we can find the best way of extracting metals and other important materials from the Earth. We can then refine these to make new, useful substances.

- The **petrochemical** industry makes fuels, plastics and other important products from oil.

- The **agrochemical** industry makes fertilizers and pesticides for farmers.

- The **pharmaceutical** industry makes drugs for the relief of pain and the treatment of disease.

*This refinery processes oil to make fuels, plastics, drugs, dyes and many other useful substances.*

Many human activities, including those of the chemical industry, have damaged our planet. Chemistry helps us to understand how environmental pollution has been caused and, in some cases, it may help us to improve the situation.

*The trees in this forest have been damaged by acid rain. The acid formed when gases from factories reacted with water in the air. We need to find a way to control sulphur dioxide and other acidic gases.*

# Pure substances and mixtures

Chemistry is the study of substances and how they behave. Therefore it is important to know when a substance is pure, and when it contains two or more different substances mixed together.

## Pure substances and mixtures

In a pure substance all the particles are the same. In a pure **element** all the atoms are identical. In a pure **compound** all the molecules are the same.

In a **mixture**, there is more than one type of particle and they are not joined together.

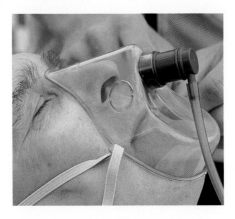

*This patient is breathing **pure oxygen**. All the oxygen molecules are the same.*

*This athlete is breathing air. Air is a **mixture** of gases. It contains molecules of oxygen, nitrogen, water, carbon dioxide, and other gases.*

## Is it pure or is it a mixture?

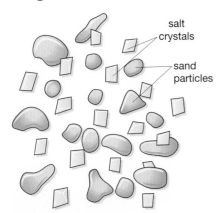

*This is a mixture of salt and sand. We can see the difference between the colour and shape of the salt crystals and the particles of sand. In some mixtures, the particles are so small and so well mixed that it all looks the same – just like a pure substance.*

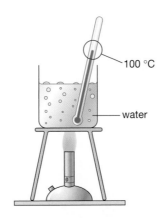

*This is pure water. We can tell because it boils at 100 °C and it melts at 0 °C. A mixture, for example salt solution, has different boiling and melting points depending on the amount of each substance in it.*

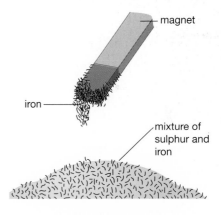

*This is a mixture of iron filings and sulphur. We can tell because the iron is attracted to the magnet, but the sulphur is left behind. Some mixtures can be easily separated like this. Pure substances are usually much more difficult to break apart.*

## Questions

1  How could you prove to a friend that soil from a garden is not a pure substance?

2  A garage sells bottles of 'pure, distilled water' for use in car batteries. Hannah buys two bottles of the water and tests them in the laboratory. The water from bottle A boils at 101 °C and the water from bottle B boils at 102 °C. What is Hannah's conclusion? Explain why.

3  Some iron filings have got mixed up with some copper powder. How could you separate them? Explain why.

# Mixtures with liquids

When we mix a solid with a liquid, we often get a mixture of the two substances. If the solid **dissolves**, we get a **solution**. If it doesn't dissolve, the solid may remain visible in the liquid.

*Salt (sodium chloride) dissolves in water. It gives a clear, colourless solution. The salt particles are still there, but they are so small that they can't be seen.*

*Copper sulphate crystals dissolve in water to give a clear, blue solution. The copper sulphate particles are still there, but they are so small that they can't be seen.*

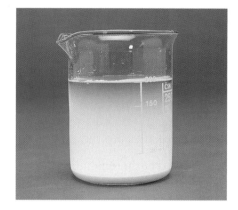

*Chalk (calcium carbonate) does not dissolve in water. Clumps of chalk particles, tiny but big enough to be seen, are **suspended** in the water. Some of the chalk has settled on the bottom of the beaker as a **sediment**.*

Water is a good solvent but it will not dissolve all substances. For example, oils and fats do not form solutions in water. These need other solvents.

It is not only solids that will dissolve. Gases can also form solutions in liquids.

| substance | solvent |
|---|---|
| gloss paint | white spirit |
| nail varnish | propanone ('acetone') |
| oil and grease | dichloromethane ('dry-cleaning fluid') |
| fragrant 'oils' in perfume and aftershave | ethanol ('alcohol') |

## Activity

1  Find out which of these common substances will dissolve in water: sugar, sand, salt, talcum powder, flour, bicarbonate of soda, cooking oil, vinegar. Make a table of your results.

2  Design and carry out an experiment to find how much sugar will dissolve in one cup of water at room temperature. How do you know when to stop adding sugar?

*This fish survives because there is oxygen gas dissolved in the water. The fish uses its gills to extract the oxygen.*

*This fizzy drink has carbon dioxide gas dissolved in it. When the bottle is opened, some of the carbon dioxide comes out of the solution as bubbles.*

# Separating solids from liquids

Chemists often need to separate one substance from another. How can you do this if you have a solid mixed with a liquid?

## Method 1 – for solids that have not dissolved

The suspended solid can be removed by pouring the mixture through **filter paper**. The liquid passes through the small holes in the paper but the solid gets trapped.

The liquid that gets through is called the **filtrate**. The solid left behind is called the **residue**.

This method is good for separating sand or chalk from water because these substances are **insoluble** in water. It can't be used to separate dissolved copper sulphate from water, because all the solution would pass through the filter.

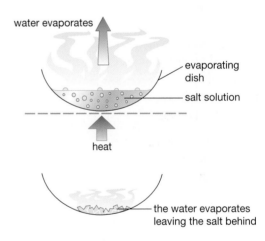

*Separating undissolved solids.*

## Method 2 – for solids that have dissolved

The liquid can be removed by heating the solution until the solvent evaporates (turns to a gas) leaving the solid behind.

This method is good for getting salt from salt solution or copper sulphate crystals from copper sulphate solution. Notice that with this method we 'lose' the water from the mixture.

Sea water is a solution of common salt (and other chemicals) in water. To get solid salt from sea water, we just heat the water until dry salt crystals are left behind.

*Separating dissolved solids.*

## A method for separating salt from sand

Salt will dissolve in water but sand will not.
How can we separate a mixture of salt and sand?

Simple…

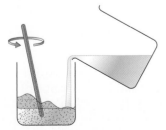

*1* **Add water** to the salt/sand mixture and stir. The salt will dissolve but the sand will not.

*2* Pour the salt/sand solution through a **filter** paper. Salt solution will go through but sand will be left in the filter.

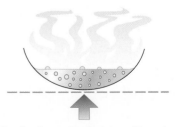

*3* Take the clear salt solution and heat it. The water will **evaporate** and you will be left with dry salt.

# Crystals from solutions

Many solids can be separated from concentrated solutions by letting them form crystals. You can recognize good crystals by their regular shapes, flat faces and sharp edges. Table salt, which chemists call sodium chloride, has crystals that are cubes. Other chemicals form different shapes, as shown below.

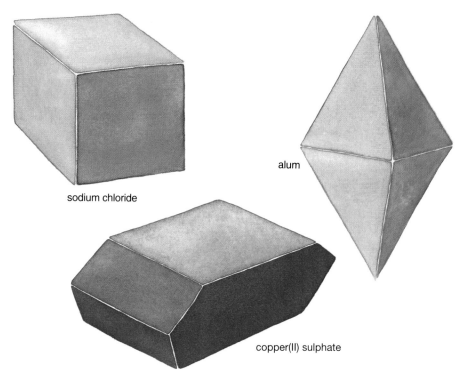

sodium chloride

alum

copper(II) sulphate

*Can you see the shape of a copper(II) sulphate crystal?*

*Salt crystals have a definite shape. They are not always easy to see. Try looking at them under a microscope.*

## Crystals from copper(II) sulphate solution

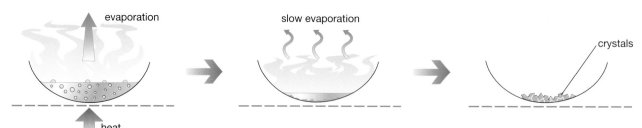

evaporation

heat

slow evaporation

crystals

**1** Heat the solution to evaporate some of the water. This makes the solution more concentrated.

**2** Stop heating when half the water has gone. Crystals will form as the solution cools, because cool water can't dissolve as much copper(II) sulphate as hot water.

**3** Leave the solution in a warm place for all the water to slowly evaporate. In the dish you will find small blue crystals of copper(II) sulphate.

**Remember to wash your hands – copper(II) sulphate is poisonous!**

# Liquids from solutions

Evaporating a solution leaves the solid behind but the liquid solvent is 'lost'. It turns into a gas and disappears into the air. We can collect the liquid using **distillation**.

## Distillation of sea water

Sea water is a solution of salts in water. When sea water is heated, water evaporates. Using distillation apparatus, the steam cools as it passes through the **condenser** and turns back into a liquid.

Pure water drips from the condenser. We can tell that it is pure because the thermometer shows 100 °C – the boiling point of water.

Water purified in this way is called **distilled water**. It is used in car batteries, in steam irons, and in chemistry laboratories.

## Distillation of alcohol solution

Alcohol (ethanol) dissolves in water to make a clear solution. To separate the two liquids, we use the fact that ethanol boils at 78 °C and water boils at 100 °C.

The method used is called **fractional distillation**. As the solution is heated, the ethanol evaporates first and, when the thermometer reads 78 °C, ethanol vapour starts to reach the condenser. It cools down and drips into the collecting beaker.

Some water does evaporate from the solution but as it rises up the fractionating column, it cools down, turns back into a liquid, and trickles back into the flask.

As long as the temperature is just 78 °C, we collect almost pure ethanol.

## Question

1 Imagine you have been shipwrecked on a desert island. You search the island but can't find any fresh water. How could you produce 'pure' water from the sea? What 'apparatus' would you construct? Explain how it would work.

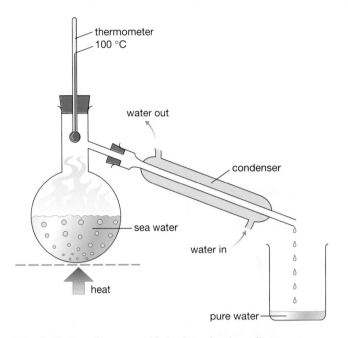

*The distillation of sea water. Notice how chemistry diagrams are drawn as a **cross-section**. This helps us to see how the apparatus works. For example, here we can see that the steam passes through the middle part of the condenser and is cooled by the cold water on the outside.*

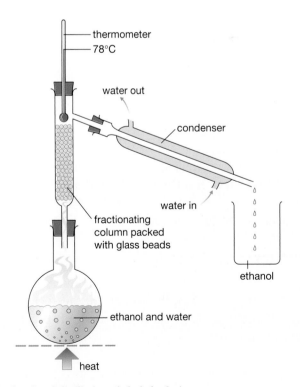

*The fractional distillation of alcohol solution.*

# Using distillation

Distillation is a very important industrial process. Perhaps its most important use is the production of ethanol (alcohol). Ethanol is present in alcoholic drinks, but it is also used as a fuel and for making many other chemicals.

## Fermentation

Fermentation takes place when sugars are used for respiration by microscopic organisms called yeasts. The yeast uses the sugar to produce energy. The products are carbon dioxide and alcohol.

$$\text{sugars} \xrightarrow{\text{yeast}} \text{ethanol (alcohol)} + \text{carbon dioxide} + \text{energy}$$

To make beer, yeast acts on the sugars in oats, barley, or other cereals. Wine is made by fermenting grapes.

Yeast can't live in very high concentrations of alcohol, so the fermentation of beer and wine eventually stops. Beer contains about 5% alcohol and wine contains about 15% alcohol – the rest is mainly water!

## Distillation of wines

The level of alcohol in an alcoholic drink can be increased by **distilling** the solution. This produces the range of drinks known as spirits. Brandy is made by distilling wine. Whisky is made by distilling the liquid from fermenting grain.

It is legal to make wine at home, but it is illegal to distil the wine to increase the level of alcohol. Only licensed **distilleries** can do this.

## Alcohol as a fuel

In some countries there is no oil and so it has to be imported. However, alcohol can be produced by fermenting sugar and then distilling the solution to make pure alcohol. This can be **blended** with petrol to make a good fuel for cars.

## Question

1  Jonathan's father makes wine at home. At first, one bubble of gas escapes through the 'air lock' every 40 seconds. After six weeks, a bubble escapes every ten minutes.
   **a)** What gas is in the bubbles?
   **b)** Suggest two reasons why the gas is produced more slowly after six weeks.

*A kit for brewing home-made wine. Fruit juice ferments in the glass jar. The special funnel keeps air out but lets carbon dioxide gas escape.*

*These are copper pot stills in a whisky distillery. After distillation, the whisky contains a higher proportion of alcohol.*

*Brazil is one country where alcohol is used as a fuel for cars.*

# Separating coloured substances

Some mixtures contain coloured substances. These can be separated using **chromatography**.

## Chromatography

Chromatography uses a **solvent** for the coloured substances and an absorbent surface for them to travel across. To separate the colours in black ink, we use water and filter paper.

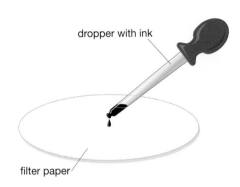

*1 Place a drop of black ink at the centre of a piece of filter paper. Let it dry.*

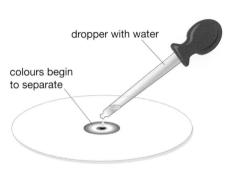

*2 Carefully squeeze small drops of water on to the ink. Leave a little time between drops, to let the ink spread out. As the water moves across the filter paper it will carry the colours with it, but different colours will move at different speeds.*

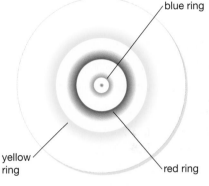

*3 In this ink there are three coloured substances: blue, red and yellow. Notice that the blue dye didn't move as fast as the others. It got left behind and so formed its own ring. Next the red stopped moving. The yellow substance was the most soluble and so moved the furthest.*

## Using chromatography

Paper chromatography can be used to investigate the chemicals in unknown substances. For example, we can use chromatography to separate the substances in mystery mixture X, at the same time comparing the results with some known chemicals: A, B, C, and D.

These substances won't dissolve in water so we use an organic solvent called **propanone**. We use a cylinder of paper so that the chemicals can rise up it without getting mixed up. This is called **ascending paper chromatography**.

From these results we can see that the mystery mixture X contains chemicals A, B and D but it doesn't contain C.

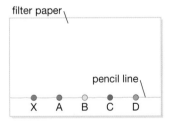

*1 Concentrated solutions of X and the known chemicals A, B, C and D are placed on a base line on a sheet of filter paper.*

*2 The paper is rolled up and stood in propanone. The propanone rises up the paper carrying the substances with it. Each substance travels a different distance.*

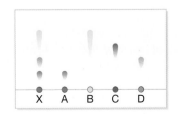

*3 X has separated into three spots which can be compared with the final positions of the known substances.*

Chemists are interested in the way in which substances change under different conditions. They divide the changes that they observe into two types: physical and chemical.

## Physical changes

Substances change when, for example, they are heated, cooled, placed under pressure or even mixed with other substances. If the change does not actually make any new substances, we say it is a physical change. Most **physical changes** are quite easy to reverse!

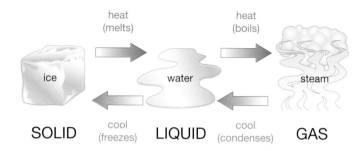

*Water's changes of state.*

## Changes of state

Many substances can exist in three forms or **states**: solid, liquid, and gas. They change from one state to another when they are heated or cooled. No new substances are formed so these are **physical changes**.

Some gases can be turned into liquids by putting them under pressure. The fuel cylinder for the camping stove in the photo contains liquid butane. When the tap is opened, the pressure is released and butane gas escapes. This is a physical change.

(When the butane burns in the air, new substances are formed. This is **not** a physical change.)

## Thermal expansion and contraction

Substances **expand** when we heat them. For example, the mercury in a thermometer expands as the temperature rises. However, when it gets colder, the mercury **contracts** and falls back to a lower reading. These changes do not make any new substances. They are just physical changes.

Solids and gases also expand when we heat them. For example, steel bridges are longer in the summer than in the winter! Such physical changes can damage the road surface, so a bridge is built with a small gap to allow it to expand and contract easily.

### Activity

1  'Expansion joints' allow structures to expand and contract without damage. Look out for them in long brick walls, at the ends of bridges, and between sections of roads.

*Bottled liquid petroleum gases (LPG) such as propane and butane are useful as portable sources of gas.*

*Expansion gap in a motorway bridge.*

# Physical changes (2)

When we mix two substances together there is a change. For example, when we mix solid, white salt crystals with water, they dissolve to give a clear solution. However, the change is only **physical**. The salt is still there and, just by evaporating the water, we can get it back.

Ethanol will dissolve in water, but because the change is physical, we can separate the liquids easily by using fractional distillation. Afterwards the ethanol and alcohol are exactly the same as they were before. For example, water still boils at 100 °C.

| mixture | separate by ... |
| --- | --- |
| chalk mixed with water | filtering |
| salt dissolved in water | evaporating the water |
| ethanol mixed with water | using fractional distillation |

## Mixing sulphur and iron

Sulphur is a yellow powder. Iron filings are small, grey-black pieces of metal. When we mix sulphur and iron together, we get a mixture in which we can still see the separate pieces of sulphur and iron.

We can separate the iron simply by using a strong magnet. The iron is attracted out of the mixture by the magnet, but the sulphur is left behind.

## Heating sulphur and iron

If we heat a mixture of sulphur and iron, a reaction takes place. The mixture glows brightly and, when it cools down, a black solid is left. All the yellow sulphur has gone and the black solid is not attracted to a magnet. A new substance has formed. This is **not** a physical change.

This is an example of a **chemical change**. The sulphur and iron have **reacted** to form a compound called iron sulphide. It is very, very difficult to get the original substances back.

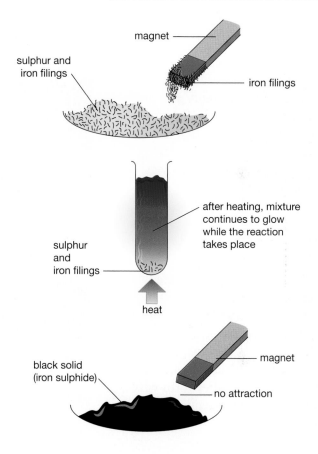

## Questions

1 Which of the following are physical changes?
   a) Water expands as it turns to ice.
   b) Steam condenses to water on a cold mirror.
   c) Methane gas burns in a gas cooker.
   d) A metal bar gets longer when it is heated.
   e) A steel bridge rusts.
   f) A steel bridge contracts on a cold winter's day.
   g) Fruit juice ferments, releasing carbon dioxide.
   h) Air is pumped into a car tyre at high pressure.

2 a) Give two differences between iron sulphide and an iron and sulphur mixture.
   b) Sulphur will dissolve in a liquid called methylbenzene but iron will not. Describe a method which uses this fact to separate iron from a mixture of sulphur and iron.

3 Ethanol dissolves in water. Ethanol burns in air. Which of these involves a chemical reaction? Give two reasons for your answer.

# Chemical changes (1)

Chemists are interested in changes where two or more substances react to form new chemicals. These are called chemical changes. The substances that are mixed are called the reactants and the new things which result are called products.

**reaction**

**reactants ⟶ products**

## Recognizing reactions

### 1  Energy changes
Many chemical reactions give out **energy**. The reactants give out heat and, sometimes, light. The burning of a match is a good example of a chemical reaction which gives out heat (**exothermic reaction**).

*This firework display is the result of chemical reactions that release light and heat.*

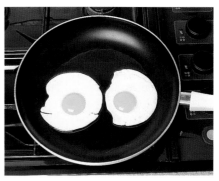

*Some chemical reactions take in energy. For example, the chemical reactions that turn a raw egg into a fried egg on a gas cooker need energy from the gas flame.*

### 2  Change in appearance
The products in a chemical reaction may look very different from the original reactants. Magnesium is a shiny metal and oxygen is a colourless gas, but when they react they form white, flaky, magnesium oxide.

*When magnesium burns in the oxygen of the air, it gives out a lot of heat and light.*

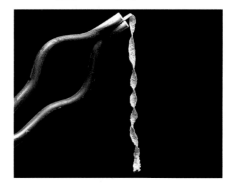

*The final product, magnesium oxide, doesn't look like magnesium or oxygen!*

### 3  Fizzing
When a reaction produces a gas, we can often see or hear fizzing as bubbles of gas escape. This is called **effervescence**.

*When an acid is added to a carbonate, for example calcium carbonate, effervescence takes place as carbon dioxide gas is given off.*

### Activity

1  Place some sodium hydrogencarbonate (baking powder) on a saucer. Add a few drops of vinegar or lemon juice (acid). Look for effervescence.

2  Also try acid with: salt, washing soda, sugar, an indigestion tablet, 'scale' from inside a kettle.

# Chemical changes (2)

The products of a chemical change may have very different physical and chemical properties to the reactants.

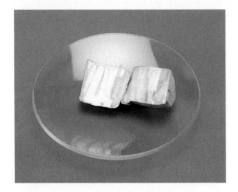

*Sodium is a soft, shiny metal. It is very reactive, especially when it comes into contact with water. In the laboratory, sodium is stored under oil and has to be handled with great care.*

*Chlorine is a yellow-green gas. It is very poisonous and was used as a chemical weapon in World War I. In the laboratory, reactions that use or produce chlorine gas are carried out in a fume cupboard.*

*When sodium and chlorine react they produce sodium chloride. This is the common salt we use on our food. It is not very reactive or poisonous. In fact it is an essential part of our diet.*

## Reversing chemical changes

Chemical changes are usually very difficult to reverse. For example, to get sodium metal and chlorine gas from salt, we have to melt the sodium chloride and then pass an electric current through it. This **electrolysis** takes a lot of energy.

Other chemical changes are even more difficult to reverse. Imagine burning a piece of wood and then trying to make a new piece of wood out of the ash and the gases produced!

*Why would these reactions be difficult to reverse?*

## Describing chemical reactions

Chemical reactions can be described by **word equations**. We list the reactants first and then the products. We use an **arrow** to show the direction of the reaction. We can also show whether heat is given out.

On the right are some examples for reactions we have studied.

- **Burning magnesium in oxygen**

  magnesium + oxygen → magnesium oxide + heat

- **Reaction of sodium with chlorine**

  sodium + chlorine → sodium chloride + heat

- **Reaction of sulphur with iron**

  sulphur + iron → iron sulphide + heat

## Questions

1  Write down **a)** three things that you might **see** and **b)** two things that you might **hear** when a chemical change takes place.

2  An **exothermic** reaction gives out heat.
**a)** Find five other words that start with 'ex' meaning 'out'.
**b)** Find five other words that contain 'therm', meaning 'heat'.

# Questions

1 **a)** Write down one product from
i) the petrochemical industry ii) the agrochemical industry and iii) the pharmaceutical industry.
**b)** Choose one of these industries. Describe two ways in which it makes life better and two ways in which it causes problems.

2 The diagram shows some water being heated over a butane gas burner.

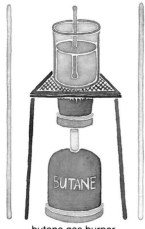

butane gas burner

Which of the following are physical changes and which are chemical changes?
**a)** Liquid butane in the container turns to butane gas as it escapes.
**b)** Butane gas burns in air and gives out heat.
**c)** Water in the container gets hotter.
**d)** Some water evaporates and turns to steam.

3 The diagram shows how a coffee-making machine works.

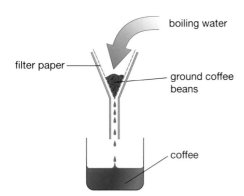

**a)** How do you know that some substances in the coffee beans are soluble?
**b)** What is the purpose of the filter paper?
**c)** What is the filtrate? What is the residue?

4 A teacher says that the black ink that she uses in her pen is mainly water with some coloured dyes. Hannah says that she will try to separate the water by distilling the ink. Owen says that he will investigate the dyes using paper chromatography.
**a)** Draw a diagram to show the apparatus that Hannah could use.
**b)** How can Hannah check whether the liquid she collects is pure water?
**c)** Explain how Owen will separate the coloured substances in the ink.

5 The diagram shows wine being made.

air lock

**a)** What is in the glass jar?
**b)** What do we call the chemical reaction that turns sugar to alcohol?
**c)** What is the gas that bubbles through the special funnel?

6 Here is the word equation for a chemical reaction:

**carbon + oxygen → carbon dioxide + heat**

**a)** What are the reactants?
**b)** What new substance is formed?
**c)** What do we call reactions, like this, that give out heat?
**d)** What does carbon look like? What does oxygen look like? What does carbon dioxide look like?
**e)** Give three differences between this chemical reaction and a physical change.

# 2 Mixtures, elements, and compounds

*What is the difference between a mixture and a pure substance?*
*What is an element?*
*What is a compound?*
*What do atoms contain?*
*How can we arrange all the elements in order?*

## Mixtures, elements and compounds

All substances are made up of small particles. Mixtures are made up of different types of particle. Pure elements and compounds only have one type of particle. The particles are too small to see, so in diagrams they are represented by small circles. This is our **model** for atoms and molecules.

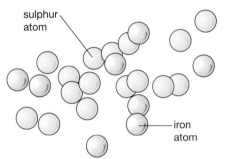

*Mixture of sulphur and iron: this is made up of separate particles of iron and sulphur. They are not joined together and are easy to separate.*

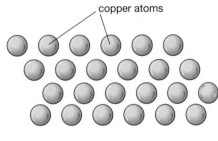

*Pure copper: all the particles are exactly the same and contain only copper atoms. This is an element. It has the symbol Cu.*

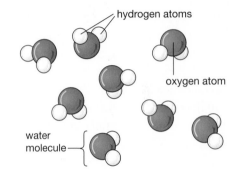

*Pure water: all the particles are exactly the same but each one contains two types of atom – hydrogen and oxygen. Water is a compound. It has the formula $H_2O$.*

**Elements** cannot be broken down into anything simpler because all the atoms are the same.

**Compounds** are made up of particles called **molecules**, which contain the atoms of different elements joined together.

Compounds can be broken down into their elements. For example, passing electricity through water ($H_2O$) breaks it down into hydrogen and oxygen.

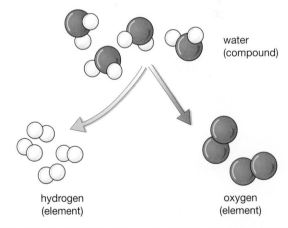

water (compound)

hydrogen (element)

oxygen (element)

There are just over 100 elements. These combine together to make the millions of different substances that make up all living and non-living things in the universe.

The table on the right shows some common elements and their symbols.

| some common elements... | | |
|---|---|---|
| *hydrogen H* | *chlorine Cl* | *lead Pb* |
| *oxygen O* | *calcium Ca* | *sodium Na* |
| *nitrogen N* | *copper Cu* | *magnesium Mg* |
| *carbon C* | *zinc Zn* | *silver Ag* |
| *sulphur S* | *iron Fe* | *gold Au* |

An atom is far too small to be seen by the naked eye. Only by using very powerful microscopes is it possible to obtain a 'picture' of an atom. If you put 100 million atoms side by side, they would only measure 1 cm across. It is very difficult to imagine anything this small. Despite these difficulties, scientists have been able to find out a great deal about atoms.

Every atom is thought to be made up of a **nucleus** surrounded by a cloud of **electrons**. The nucleus consists of **protons** and **neutrons**.

## Atomic number

The number of protons in an atom is called its **atomic number**. Each element has a different atomic number. Elements contain neutral atoms. Protons are positively charged particles, so there must also be negatively charged particles in an atom. These negatively charged particles are electrons. The number of electrons is equal to the number of protons in an element, so the atomic number also tells us how many electrons the atom has.

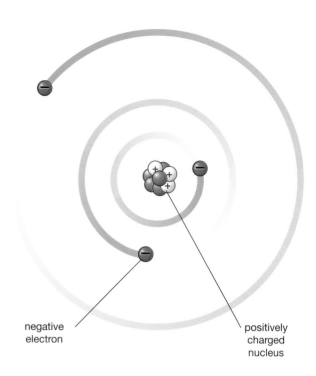

negative electron

positively charged nucleus

*Theoretical model of the atom*

## Mass number

Protons and neutrons have approximately the same mass. Electrons have a mass close to zero. The mass of an atom depends on how many protons and neutrons it has:

$$\frac{\textbf{mass number}}{\textbf{(or nucleon number)}} = \frac{\textbf{number of protons}}{\textbf{+ neutrons in an atom}}$$

From this it follows that:

**mass number − atomic number = number of neutrons**

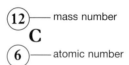

mass number

C

atomic number

*C is the symbol for the element carbon.*
*All carbon atoms have six protons in the nucleus.*
*This carbon atom has six protons and six neutrons, giving a mass of 12.*

## Models of simple atoms

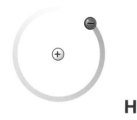

**H**

*This is the simplest of all atoms. It has just one electron orbiting one proton. The element is* **hydrogen**.

**He**

*This atom has two electrons orbiting two protons and two neutrons. The element is* **helium**.

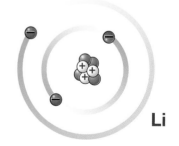

**Li**

*This atom has three electrons orbiting three protons and four neutrons. The element is* **lithium**.

# The arrangement of electrons

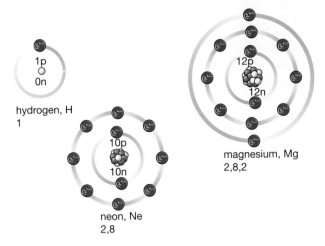

*The arrangement of electrons in three different atoms*

Scientists have worked out a theoretical model of the atom in which the electrons are arranged in definite layers or levels of energy around the nucleus. Each layer or **shell** can hold a certain number of electrons. The first **energy shell**, which is at the lowest energy level, can hold a maximum of two electrons. The second and third shells can hold a maximum of eight electrons each. The electrons build up from the first shell, filling each one until all the electrons are in place. This means that the atom has the minimum amount of energy and all the electrons are as close to the nucleus as they can be. The table below shows how the electrons are arranged for the first 20 elements.

| element | symbol | atomic number | number of electrons | first shell | second shell | third shell | fourth shell |
|---|---|---|---|---|---|---|---|
| hydrogen | H | 1 | 1 | 1 | | | |
| helium | He | 2 | 2 | 2 | | | |
| lithium | Li | 3 | 3 | 2 | 1 | | |
| beryllium | Be | 4 | 4 | 2 | 2 | | |
| boron | B | 5 | 5 | 2 | 3 | | |
| carbon | C | 6 | 6 | 2 | 4 | | |
| nitrogen | N | 7 | 7 | 2 | 5 | | |
| oxyygen | O | 8 | 8 | 2 | 6 | | |
| fluorine | F | 9 | 9 | 2 | 7 | | |
| neon | Ne | 10 | 10 | 2 | 8 | | |
| sodium | Na | 11 | 11 | 2 | 8 | 1 | |
| magnesium | Mg | 12 | 12 | 2 | 8 | 2 | |
| aluminium | Al | 13 | 13 | 2 | 8 | 3 | |
| silicon | Si | 14 | 14 | 2 | 8 | 4 | |
| phosphorus | P | 15 | 15 | 2 | 8 | 5 | |
| sulphur | S | 16 | 16 | 2 | 8 | 6 | |
| chlorine | Cl | 17 | 17 | 2 | 8 | 7 | |
| argon | Ar | 18 | 18 | 2 | 8 | 8 | |
| potassium | K | 19 | 19 | 2 | 8 | 8 | 1 |
| calcium | Ca | 20 | 20 | 2 | 8 | 8 | 2 |

## What are ions?

In some chemical reactions, the electrons that surround the nucleus move from one atom to another. An atom with one or more additional electrons is called a **negative ion**; an atom which has lost one or more electrons is called a **positive ion**. Metal atoms lose electrons in chemical reactions so their atoms become ions with a positive charge. Non-metal atoms accept these extra electrons to become negatively charged ions.

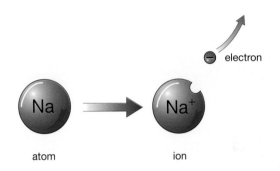

*Sodium is a metal. Each sodium ion can lose one electron to become a positively charged **ion**.*

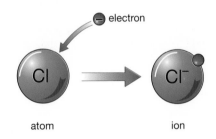

*Chlorine atoms gain an electron to become negatively charged **ions**.*

## Questions

**1** Explain the following terms: **atomic number, mass number, ion**.

**2** Gold has atomic number 79 and mass number 197. What would you find inside an atom of gold?

**3** Draw a labelled diagram to show the structure of an oxygen atom. (Oxygen has atomic number 8 and mass number 16.)

**4** All carbon atoms have atomic number 6, but some have mass number 12 and others have mass number 14. What is **a)** the same and **b)** different about the structures of these two types of carbon atom?

# Modern periodic tables

There are over 100 different elements, each with different physical and chemical properties. The table displays all the elements in horizontal rows called **periods** and vertical columns called **groups**. The elements are in the order of their atomic numbers. This is the modern **periodic table**.

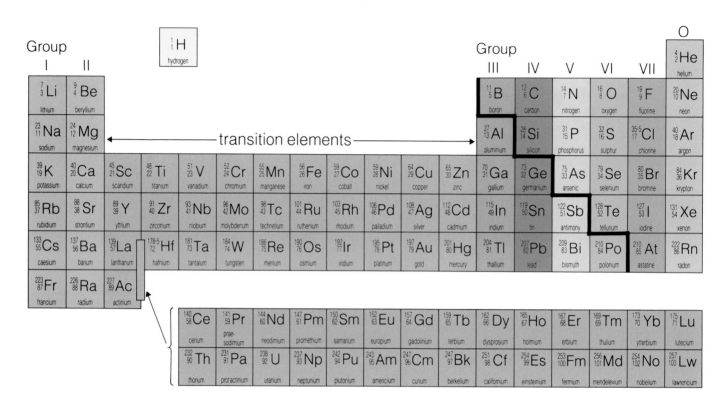

*The periodic table of the elements*

Notice that hydrogen is outside the main table. It does not fit in any particular group.

Elements within a group share similar properties. The groups are numbered, starting at group I on the left-hand side. The elements in group I are called the **alkali metals** and they include lithium, Li, sodium, Na, and potassium, K. The elements in group II are sometimes called the **alkaline earth metals**. Calcium, Ca, and magnesium, Mg, are in this group. Between groups II and III, in the fourth period, there is a large group called the **transition elements**. The last group is called 0, the **noble gases**, including helium, He, neon, Ne, argon, Ar, and krypton, Kr.

Each of the elements in the periodic table is shown by a symbol, a number above it, and a number below it. The smaller number, the lower one, is the **atomic number**. This gives information about the number of positive and negative particles in an atom. The larger number, the upper one, is the **relative atomic mass** –

it shows how that element's mass compares with the mass of other elements. This is explained on page 22.

relative atomic mass —— 19 $F$

atomic number —— 9

**fluorine**

## Questions

**1 a)** Write down the group numbers for carbon, oxygen, nitrogen, and sulphur.
**b)** Write down the group numbers for sodium, magnesium, and calcium.

**2** Where in the periodic table do you find the precious metals gold, silver, and platinum?

**3** Write down the names of the elements having these symbols:

Pb    Sn    W    K    P    Hg

# Metals and non-metals

There are two types of elements, **metals** and **non-metals**. There are many more **metal** elements than **non-metal** elements. The metals are on the left-hand side of the periodic table, the non-metals on the right. They are separated on the periodic table by a stepped line. The metals close to this line have some of the properties of the non-metals. Similarly, the non-metals close to the line have some metallic properties. The properties of metals and non-metals are shown in the table below.

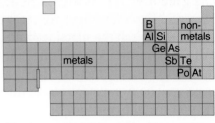

*Metals are on the left-hand side of the periodic table and non-metals on the right.*

| metals | non-metals |
|---|---|
| usually solids at room temperature | usually solids or gases at room temperature |
| good conductors of electricity and heat | do not usually conduct heat or electricity |
| lustrous (shiny) | not usually shiny |
| malleable (can be hammered into a different shape) | brittle when solid and shatter when hammered |
| ductile (can be stretched) | too brittle to be stretched |
| usually sonorous (ring like a bell when hit) | not sonorous |
| usually very dense | generally have a low density |
| nearly all have high melting points | have low melting points, with a few exceptions |
| When they react with dilute acids, hydrogen gas is given off | do not react with dilute acids |

*Properties of metal and non-metal elements*

*There are far more metals than non-metals.*

## Questions

**1** Choose two metals which you are familiar with, e.g. copper and iron, and look at them closely. What kind of properties would you use to describe them?

**2** Oxygen and sulphur are two non-metals. How do their properties differ from those of metals?

**3** Using the headings below, make a list of uses for some metals and non-metals. One is done for you.

| element | symbol | used for | reason for using it |
|---|---|---|---|
| copper | Cu | water pipes | does not rust, easily bent into shape, can be joined by soldering |

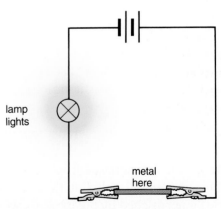

*When a metal is placed in an electric circuit containing a bulb, the bulb lights. Metals conduct electricity. If a piece of sulphur was placed in the same circuit, what would happen?*

The general properties of metals and non-metals apply to nearly all the elements. However, there are exceptions. For example, silicon, Si, is a shiny non-metal; the metal lead, Pb, is not sonorous; group I metals have low densities and melting points, and iodine, I, has a higher density than many metals. Metals and non-metals are all either solids or gases. The two exceptions to this are the metal **mercury**, Hg, and the non-metal **bromine**, Br. They are both liquids at room temperature. The properties of bromine are shown on page 29. The properties of mercury are shown in the table below.

## Mercury

| atomic number | 80 |
| atomic mass | 201 |
| melting point | $-39\,°C$ |
| boiling point | $357\,°C$ |
| density | $13.55\,g\,cm^{-3}$ |

Mercury is a very dense silvery liquid with many uses. The electrolysis of brine in the manufacture of chlorine and sodium hydroxide uses mercury as the negative electrode in the cell.

However, efforts are being made to develop a new method for this process without using mercury, since leakages from cells have caused pollution problems. Mercury is used in thermometers covering a range of $0\,°C$ to $100\,°C$. Mercury expands evenly as the temperature rises and it is a good conductor of heat. It is also used in barometers to measure changes in air pressure. As the weather changes, so does the air pressure.

Other metals such as aluminium mix easily with mercury to form **alloys** which are called **amalgams**. Tooth fillings used to be made with an amalgam of mercury with tin and silver. This is now rare because if mercury is absorbed into the body, it can cause brain damage. Hatters used to use mercury to make top hats and were exposed a great deal to the metal. This may explain the expression 'mad as a hatter'!

*The 'Mad Hatter' from* Alice in Wonderland

## Mercury pollution

It is now known that exposure to mercury can cause serious health problems. It is no longer used in school laboratories. If you break a mercury thermometer, it must be cleared up by someone who knows how to do this safely.

About 40 years ago, mercury was discharged into the Minimata Bay in Japan by a local factory. It was noticed that the local fisherman became very tired and suffered from headaches. This soon spread to the rest of the community, including the population of cats. The fish in the bay had become poisoned by the mercury, which was passed on to the people who ate the fish. Many people died or suffered severe nervous disabilities.

*Mercury poisoning can have devastating effects.*

# Families of elements (1): group I

## The alkali metals

The members of group I, the alkali metals, are:

**lithium**    **Li**
**sodium**    **Na**
**potassium**  **K**
**rubidium**   **Rb**
**caesium**    **Cs**

This group is found on the far left of the periodic table. They are all metals. Group I elements are sometimes called the alkali metals because they react with water to form an alkali, as you will see on the next page. The metals are all very reactive, and because of this, they must be stored under oil to protect them from coming into contact with either air or water. It is because of this high reactivity that the alkali metals are only found naturally combined with other elements. They show similar physical properties (see table below). For example, they are shiny, conduct electricity, and have other metallic properties. However, they also have some properties that are not usually associated with the majority of metals. Lithium, sodium, and potassium each have a density which is less than that of water ($1\,g/cm^3$). This means that they float on water. Both their melting and boiling points are lower than expected for metals. One other unexpected property is that the alkali metals are soft – they can be easily cut with a knife. When they are first cut, you can see how shiny they are. After a few minutes they become very dull due to reaction with the air.

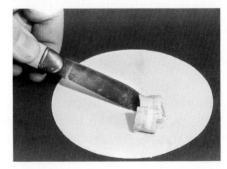

*Sodium, potassium, and lithium are stored under oil.*

*When the alkali metals are first cut, the surface is shiny. It rapidly tarnishes as the metal reacts with the air.*

| element | relative atomic mass | melting point in °C | boiling point in °C | density in g/cm³ |
|---------|---------------------|---------------------|---------------------|------------------|
| Li | 6.9 | 180 | 1331 | 0.53 |
| Na | 23.0 | 98 | 890 | 0.97 |
| K | 39.1 | 63 | 766 | 0.86 |
| Rb | 85.5 | 39 | 701 | 1.5 |

## Questions

**1** Plot a graph of melting point against relative atomic mass for the alkali metals. On the same graph, plot the boiling points. Write a sentence to describe the information the graph gives you.

**2** Look at the table of electronic configurations on page 23. Write down the arrangement of electrons in lithium, sodium, and potassium. Do you notice any trend? Write a sentence to explain what you have found.

**3** 'The alkali metals are all typical metals.' Explain why this statement is not completely correct.

# Chemical properties of group I

## Reaction with water

The alkali metals are very reactive. They are stored under oil because they tarnish quickly when exposed to moist air. Clean alkali metals react violently with water. When placed in cold water, they react immediately. They move rapidly about the surface of the water and give off hydrogen gas. The heat given off during the reaction makes the metals melt. Potassium bursts into a lilac flame. Sodium fizzes violently and may burst into a yellow flame. (Potassium is more reactive than sodium.)

The reaction produces a strongly alkaline solution.

For example:

sodium + water → hydrogen + sodium hydroxide
solution

## Combustion

The alkali metals burn in air with characteristic coloured flames.

They will also burn in chlorine, producing lots of white smoke. When sodium burns, the white smoke is small particles of sodium chloride (salt).

sodium + chlorine → sodium chloride

## Uses

The pure alkali metals are too reactive to have many uses. Liquid sodium is used as a coolant in nuclear power stations. This is because it has a low melting point and is a very good conductor of heat.

Sodium vapour is used in street lamps. Sodium lamps give an orange glow.

Sodium chloride is a very important chemical. It is used in cooking, as a food preservative, to treat icy roads, and to make sodium metal and its compounds.

Sodium hydroxide is a powerful alkali. It is used in making soaps and for cleaning ovens and greasy machine parts. Great care must be taken when using concentrated sodium hydroxide solution (caustic soda).

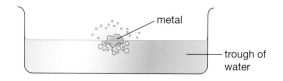

*The alkali metals react vigorously with water.*

lithium            sodium            potassium

increasing reactivity

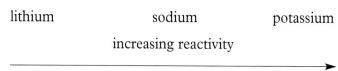

*The order of reactivity of the alkali metals.*

lithium            sodium            potassium
(red)              (yellow)          (lilac)

*Flame colours of the alkali metals.*

gas jar of chlorine

burning metal in combustion spoon

*Burning alkali metals in chlorine.*

## Questions

1  **a)** Write a word equation for the reaction of potassium with water.
   **b)** Is the reaction exothermic? Explain.

2  Find the element rubidium (Rb) on the periodic table.
   **a)** What will be produced when rubidium reacts with water? Explain how you know.
   **b)** Will the reaction be more or less vigorous than that for sodium? Explain your answer.

3  **a)** Give three reasons why students are not allowed to experiment with potassium metal and water.
   **b)** Give two safety precautions that the teacher should take when demonstrating the reaction.

# Families of elements (2): group VII

## The halogens

Halogens form a group of elements on the right of the periodic table. The first four halogens are fairly common:

| | | | |
|---|---|---|---|
| fluorine | F | bromine | Br |
| chlorine | Cl | iodine | I |

The first three elements are very reactive at room temperature. Halogens are all non-metals. As a group of elements they show trends in their physical properties – going down the group, their melting points, boiling points, and densities increase. Bromine is a liquid at room temperature and iodine is a solid. Iodine turns (almost) directly into a vapour when it is heated; it **sublimes**. This can be very dangerous in a school laboratory, especially if the vapour comes into contact with broken skin or your eyes. When using iodine, always wear safety spectacles. The other halogens are very dangerous to use in the laboratory and should only be used in a fume cupboard by a teacher.

Chlorine gas is poisonous and has been used as a chemical weapon. Here, a soldier of World War I and his horses are prepared for a gas attack.

| element | relative atomic mass | appearance at room temperature | melting point in °C | boiling point in °C | density in g/dm³ |
|---|---|---|---|---|---|
| fluorine | 19.0 | pale yellow gas | −220 | −188 | 1.69 |
| chlorine | 35.5 | pale green gas | −101 | − 35 | 3.21 |
| bromine | 79.9 | red-brown liquid | −7 | 58 | 2930 |
| iodine | 126.9 | dark grey solid | 114 | 183 | 4930 |

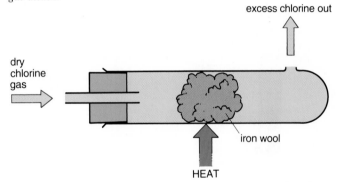

The iron wool is heated and the Bunsen removed before passing the chlorine gas through the combustion tube. This experiment needs to be carried out in a fume cupboard. Why?

## Chemical properties of group VII

The halogen elements are very reactive. When chlorine reacts with water it forms a mixture of acids which have strong bleaching properties. Household **bleaches** contain chlorine compounds.

| chlorine | + | water | → | hydrochloric acid | + | hypochlorous acid |
|---|---|---|---|---|---|---|
| $Cl_2$ | + | $H_2O$ | → | HCl | + | HClO |

Bromine does not react as easily as chlorine, and iodine only dissolves slightly in water.

Chlorine is a very reactive non-metal. It will react with all metals (even unreactive gold), to form metal chlorides. For example, if dry chlorine gas is passed over heated iron wool, as in the apparatus shown above, iron(III) chloride is produced. Bromine and iodine react in a similar way, but need a great deal more heat for a reaction to take place.

### Activities

1   Household bleaches usually contain a compound of chlorine called sodium hypochlorite. **They must be handled with extreme care and safety spectacles must be worn when using them. Do not let bleach come into contact with your skin or clothing**.

Carry out a survey of as many different bleaches as you can find. List the chemical contents of the bleach.

2   Collect $10 \, cm^3$ samples of two different household bleaches.
Add water to the samples to make $50 \, cm^3$ solutions of each sample.
See how effective each sample is by testing it on different fabrics.

# Uses of the halogens

Fluorine and chlorine are both very poisonous gases. Chlorine was used in the First World War as a chemical weapon. It has a pungent, irritating smell and must be treated with extreme care.

Because of their high reactivity the halogens as elements do not have many uses. Chlorine is an exception, as both it and its compounds have a great many uses. Its bleaching and disinfecting properties are used when chlorine is added in small quantities to drinking water. It kills the bacteria in the water without harming people or animals. Larger quantities are added to swimming pools.

A great deal of the chlorine produced is used to make **hydrochloric acid**. Chlorine is burnt in hydrogen to produce hydrogen chloride, which then dissolves very easily in water to produce the acid. This acid is used in the manufacture of many other chemicals. Other uses of halogen compounds are shown in the diagram below.

*Why does this swimmer wear goggles?*

## Environmental danger!

Some halogen compounds damage the environment. CFCs (chlorofluorocarbons) and HCFCs (hydrochlorofluorocarbons) are used in aerosols, fridges, and some packaging foams. In the atmosphere, these gases break down the ozone layer that protects us from the Sun's ultraviolet radiation.

### Activities

**1** Plot a graph of melting point against relative atomic mass for the halogens. Put the relative atomic mass on the horizontal axis and the melting point on the vertical axis. Use a relative atomic mass scale from 1 to 130 and melting point scale from −220°C to 200°C. Plot the boiling points on the same axes. What do you notice?

### Questions

**1** Does the reactivity of the halogens increase or decrease going down the group? Support your answer with suitable examples.

**2** Explain what you would expect to see if bromine water was added to a solution of potassium iodide. Write an equation to illustrate your answer.

**3** Look at the table on page 23. What is the pattern in the arrangement of electrons in group VII elements?

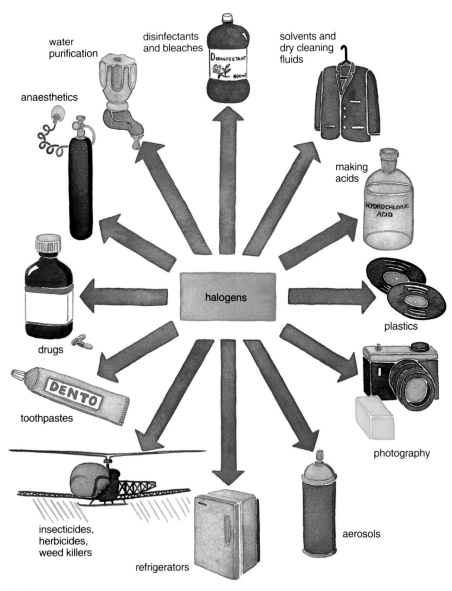

water purification

disinfectants and bleaches

solvents and dry cleaning fluids

anaesthetics

making acids

halogens

plastics

drugs

toothpastes

photography

insecticides, herbicides, weed killers

refrigerators

aerosols

*Halogens have many uses.*

# Other families of elements

There are other groups of elements in the periodic table which have similar properties to each other. Here are some examples.

## Group 0, the noble gases

| | | | |
|---|---|---|---|
| helium | He | krypton | Kr |
| neon | Ne | xenon | Xe |
| argon | Ar | radon | Rn |

The gases in this group do not react easily and do not form molecules. This is because their electron energy shells are completely full. They are so unreactive that they used to be called the **inert gases**. However, chemists have now managed to make a small number of compounds so the name has been changed to the **noble gases**.

These elements are of limited use. Argon is used to fill light bulbs since it does not react with the hot filament. Similarly, neon is used in fluorescent tubes. Helium can be used in airships because it is non-flammable and has a low density. It is safer to use than hydrogen which forms an explosive mixture with air.

*The noble gases help to create colourful light displays.*

*Helium is safe and much lighter than air – it is used for balloons.*

## Group II, the alkaline earth metals

| | | | |
|---|---|---|---|
| beryllium | Be | strontium | Sr |
| magnesium | Mg | barium | Ba |
| calcium | Ca | radium | Ra |

All the members of this group are metals. They are less reactive than the group I elements. The reactivity of the group II metals increases as you go down the group – compare the reactivities of magnesium and calcium in cold water. Calcium reacts fairly quickly in cold water giving off hydrogen gas and forming an alkali, calcium hydroxide.

$$\text{calcium} + \text{water} \rightarrow \text{calcium hydroxide} + \text{hydrogen}$$
$$\text{Ca} + 2\text{H}_2\text{O} \rightarrow \text{Ca(OH)}_2 + 2\text{H}_2$$

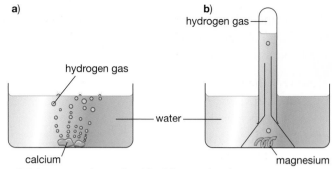

*a Calcium reacts vigorously with cold water, in minutes.*

*b Magnesium reacts very slowly with cold water. This experiment needs to be set up and left for a few days before there is enough hydrogen to test.*

Clean magnesium reacts slowly with cold water, but reacts more quickly with steam to form magnesium hydroxide and hydrogen. Magnesium is a very useful metal. It is very light, and is used extensively in making alloys (see page 45). Since magnesium burns with a very bright light it is used in fireworks and flares.

*When burning magnesium in the laboratory, it is important not to look directly at the brilliant white light. Some fireworks contain magnesium.*

Calcium compounds have important uses:

| calcium compound | common name | use |
|---|---|---|
| calcium sulphate | gypsum | making 'plaster of Paris', wall and ceiling plaster, plasterboard, etc. |
| calcium hydroxide | lime | neutralizing acid soils |
| calcium phosphate | | fertilizer |
| calcium carbonate | limestone | making cement |

# Using the periodic table

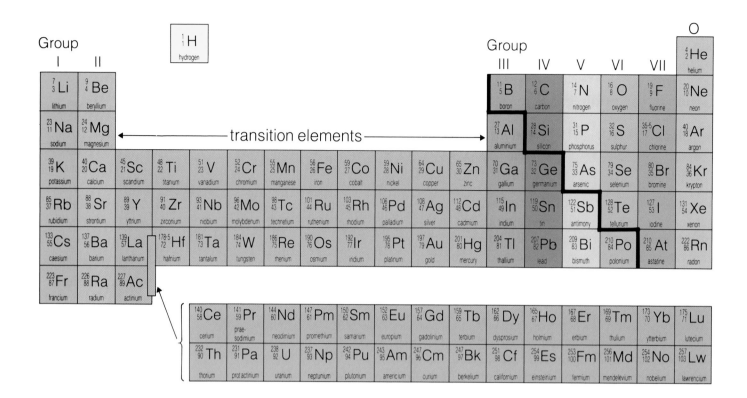

If you know what group of the periodic table an element is in, you can predict how it will react. For example, if you are told that an element is in group I of the periodic table, you will know that it is a metal which reacts violently with cold water. You should also be able to predict its physical properties, since all group I elements can be easily cut with a knife and have low densities.

If the properties and reactions of an element are known it is also possible to predict which group of the periodic table it is in. For example, if you are told that an element is a gas at room temperature, doesn't seem to react with any other elements, and exists as a molecule with only one atom in, then you could suggest that it is likely to be in group 0.

By knowing how many electrons there are in the outside shell of an atom, it is possible to say which group of the periodic table it is in. From this information you can predict its likely reactions and properties.

*The halogens become less reactive going down the group. Fluorine is the most reactive and iodine the least reactive.*

## Questions

**1** Predict the reactions and properties of the following elements:

**a)** element X in group II

**b)** element Y, a metal which reacts quite vigorously with dilute acids but not with cold water. Its compounds are all white solids and are insoluble in water.

**c)** element Z which has seven electrons in its outside shell.

# Elements, atoms, and molecules

Elements only contain one type of atom. However, sometimes two or more of these join together to form a molecule. We can use our model of the atom to represent the structures of the elements.

## Group 0 elements

The group 0 elements are not reactive. Their outermost electron shells are completely full and so they can't lose, gain, or share electrons easily. The atoms can't join together and so their 'molecules' contain just one atom.

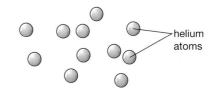

*Helium 'molecules' are single helium atoms. The formula for helium is He. The other group 0 gases (Ne, Ar, Kr, Xe, Rn) also have **monatomic** molecules.*

## Hydrogen, oxygen and nitrogen

The outer electron shells of these common elements are not full. Their atoms become more stable by joining together to form molecules. Each molecule contains two atoms of the element.

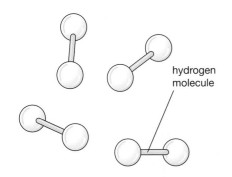

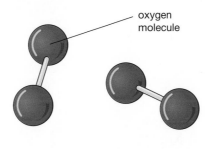

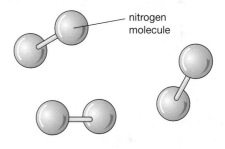

*One molecule of hydrogen contains two hydrogen atoms joined together. The formula of hydrogen gas is $H_2$.*

*One molecule of oxygen contains two oxygen atoms joined together. The formula of oxygen gas is $O_2$.*

*One molecule of nitrogen contains two nitrogen atoms joined together. The formula of nitrogen gas is $N_2$.*

## Sulphur

The atoms of some elements form much bigger groups. In one form of the element sulphur, each molecule consists of a ring of eight atoms. The formula is $S_8$.

### Questions

**1** Why don't the atoms in neon gas join up in the same way that hydrogen atoms do?

**2** Ozone has the formula $O_3$.
   **a)** Draw a diagram of an ozone molecule.
   **b)** Is ozone an element?
   Explain your answer.

**3** Carbon can form rings with the formula $C_6$. Draw a diagram of a $C_6$ molecule.

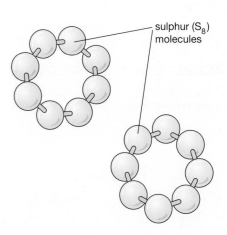

*The eight-atom ring of sulphur.*

# Combining elements (1)

Elements can combine during chemical reactions. When two or more elements join they form a **compound**. The molecules of the compound are all the same, but they contain atoms of more than one element.

*Hot sodium reacts vigorously with chlorine gas.*

## Ionic compounds

Some atoms lose or gain electrons easily to become charged ions. Positive and negative ions can be held together by electrostatic attraction. For example, in the reaction between sodium and chlorine, positive sodium ions and negative chloride ions are produced. These bond to give the compound sodium chloride.

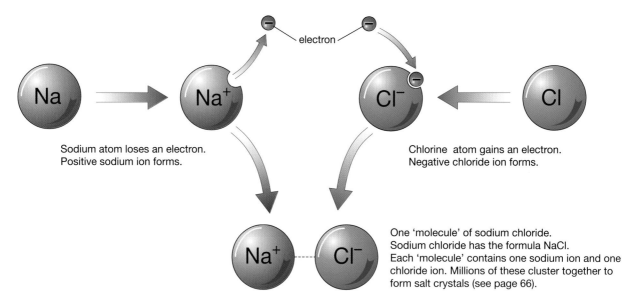

Sodium atom loses an electron.
Positive sodium ion forms.

Chlorine atom gains an electron.
Negative chloride ion forms.

One 'molecule' of sodium chloride.
Sodium chloride has the formula NaCl.
Each 'molecule' contains one sodium ion and one chloride ion. Millions of these cluster together to form salt crystals (see page 66).

*The reaction between sodium and chlorine.*

## Magnesium and oxygen

Magnesium burns very brightly in oxygen. The product is the white, powdery, solid magnesium oxide. This is an ionic compound.

Because magnesium is in group II of the periodic table, it forms an ion with two positive charges. Oxide (oxygen) ions have two negative charges.

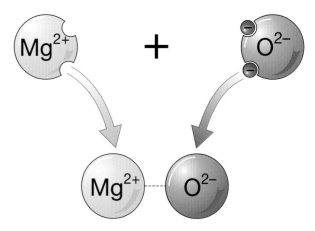

One molecule of magnesium oxide.
Magnesium oxide has the formula MgO.
Each molecule contains one magnesium ion and one oxide ion.

## Questions

**1** Which of the following are elements and which are compounds?

MgO   Ar   NaCl   $Cl_2$   $N_2$   $S_8$   He   $H_2O$

**2** Explain, using diagrams, how potassium forms the compound KBr when it reacts with bromine.

# Combining elements (2)

When two or more non-metallic elements react, they do not form ionic bonds. Instead their atoms 'overlap' so that they can share electrons. This forms strong, **covalent** bonds.

## Hydrogen chloride

One hydrogen atom can share its electron with one chlorine atom. This gives the hydrogen two electrons in its outer electron shell, and gives the chlorine eight electrons in its outer shell.

One molecule of hydrogen chloride.
Hydrogen chloride has the formula HCl.
Each molecule contains one hydrogen atom and one chlorine atom.

*Hydrogen chloride*

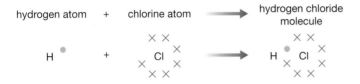

## Hydrogen oxide (water)

When water forms, two hydrogen atoms share their electrons with a single oxygen atom. This gives each hydrogen atom two electrons, and the oxygen now has eight electrons in its outer shell.

One molecule of water (hydrogen oxide).
Water has the formula $H_2O$.
Each molecule contains two hydrogen atoms and one oxygen atom.

*Hydrogen oxide*

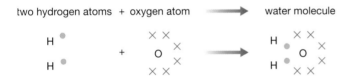

## Carbon dioxide

When carbon burns in oxygen, carbon dioxide is produced. Carbon shares electrons with two oxygen atoms. Two covalent bonds are formed.

One molecule of carbon dioxide.
Carbon dioxide has the formula $CO_2$.
Each molecule contains two oxygen atoms and one carbon atom.

*Carbon dioxide*

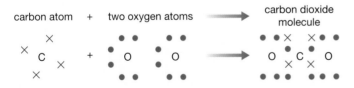

### Questions

1  Which of the following compounds are held together by covalent bonds and which are held together by ionic bonds? (Hint: Are there any metals?)

NaBr   MgS   CaO   $SO_2$   KCl   CO   $NH_3$

2  A methane molecule has the formula $CH_4$.
   **a)** What elements are in methane?
   **b)** How many atoms of each element are there in one molecule of methane?
   **c)** Use a 'cross and dot' diagram to show how four covalent bonds are formed by sharing electrons in methane.

1   Draw a diagram to show the structure of an atom of the element represented by this symbol:

$^{14}_{7}N$

Show the number of neutrons, protons, and electrons on your diagram.

2   Use the periodic table to find the names and symbols of:

**a)**  Three elements named after people.

**b)**  Three elements named after countries.

**c)**  One element named after a continent.

**d)**  One element named after a planet.

3   This question refers to the outline of the periodic table below. The letters on this table are **not** the symbols of the elements.

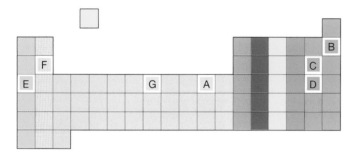

**a)**  Which element is a very unreactive gas?

**b)**  Which element reacts violently with cold water?

**c)**  Which two elements would you expect to have very similar chemical properties?

**d)**  Which two elements are 'transition metals'?

**e)**  Element D is a brown, reactive liquid. What does element C look like?

**f)**  Which element has two electrons in its outer shell?

4   An atom of uranium can be represented by this symbol:

$^{238}_{92}U$

Find the number of **a)** protons and **b)** neutrons in one atom of uranium.

5   Write word equations for the reactions described here:

**a)**  "When we put the potassium metal on the water, it fizzed and moved around the bowl. It fizzed because it was giving off hydrogen. It got so hot that it burst into flames. After it was over, the water had changed to an alkaline solution of potassium hydroxide."

**b)**  "The teacher heated the sodium on a special spoon and then placed it in a jar of chlorine gas in the fume cupboard. There was a bright flame and lots of white smoke. This was tiny particles of sodium chloride or salt."

6   Here are the molecules of some elements. Which one could be:

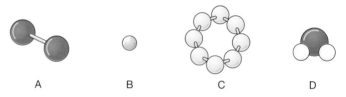

A          B          C          D

**a)**  A helium molecule?

**b)**  A water molecule?

**c)**  A sulphur molecule?

**d)**  An oxygen molecule?

7   These diagrams represent the electrons in the outer shells of carbon and hydrogen. Use them to explain how covalent bonds are formed to hold one molecule of methane ($CH_4$) together.

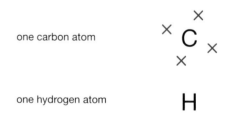

one carbon atom

one hydrogen atom

8   Using the 'ball' model for an atom, draw pictures to represent one molecule of:

**a)**  Carbon monoxide, $CO$.

**b)**  Sulphur dioxide, $SO_2$.

**c)**  Hydrogen sulphide, $H_2S$.

**d)**  Hydrogen sulphate, $H_2SO_4$.

# 3  Materials from the Earth

*Where do we get the materials we use in everyday life?*
*How do we produce pure materials?*
*Why are metals so important in the modern world?*
*How can we conserve our reserves of metals and other materials?*
*How are new materials changing the world?*

Many of our materials come from inside the Earth, from the seas, or from the atmosphere around us. Some can be used just as they are. Others have to be **refined** before we can benefit from them.

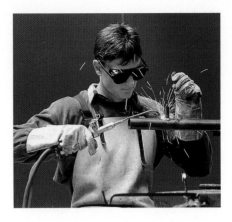

*Pure oxygen extracted from the air has many applications. Here it is being used to give a very hot flame for welding.*

## Gases from the air

Air is a mixture of gases. These can be separated so that the pure gases can be utilized. From air we get oxygen, nitrogen, and some important 'rare' gases such as neon and argon.

## Metals from the Earth

Lumps of pure gold can be found in rocks, but other metals are combined with various substances. Rocks that contain metal compounds are called **ores**. After the ore has been mined, it has to be refined.

*The ore being mined here is **bauxite**. An electrical method (**electrolysis**) is used to extract pure, shiny aluminium from the bauxite. Notice how mining can damage the environment.*

## Minerals

Rocks contain important materials. Some, for example granite, are used for building. Others are processed to produce useful substances. For example, rock salt can be processed to make sodium and chlorine.

*These chalk cliffs contain **calcium carbonate**, an ingredient in cement. It is also used, with sand, to make glass, and in the extraction of iron from iron ore. Calcium carbonate is a very important material.*

## Fossil fuels

Most of the fuel we use in our homes, cars, and factories comes from the Earth. Coal is **mined** and then either burnt or turned into 'smokeless fuel'. Oil is refined to produce petrol and other fuels. Natural gas (methane) is piped to power stations and homes. Coal, oil, and natural gas are all **fossil fuels**.

*This platform is extracting oil from the rocks beneath the sea. A pipeline then takes the oil to the mainland. (The flame is burning methane gas. Methane is often found above deposits of oil.)*

# Extracting metals from their ores

## Metal ores

An ore is a rock or mineral that contains a metal (usually in the form of an oxide). Most of the metals in use today are found combined with other chemicals as ores in the Earth's crust. The names of some ores are given in the table opposite. People mine ores to extract the metals, and some ores are running out. We need to think of ways to make more economical use of our natural resources, for example through recycling (see pages 61-2). More metal has been used by our society since 1950 than in the previous history of the world.

| name of ore | metal it contains |
| --- | --- |
| haematite | iron |
| chalcopyrite (copper pyrites) | copper (and iron) |
| malachite | copper |
| litharge | lead |
| galena | lead |
| bauxite | aluminium |
| alumina | aluminium |

There are three main stages in obtaining metals from their ores:

- mining

- extraction

- purification.

A few unreactive metals are found uncombined with other elements, for example gold is mined straight from the ground. The decision as to whether it is worth mining an ore is based on many factors such as:

- How much ore is there?

- How much will it cost to mine?

- How much will the extraction cost?

- Does someone want to buy the metal?

- How much profit is there?

- What environmental problems are there?

*Copper pyrites ore*

## Extraction methods

There are three main methods of extracting pure metals from their ores: electrolysis, reduction, or roasting in air. The method used depends on the metal.

Very reactive metals such as sodium and aluminium require a great deal of energy to separate them from their compounds. **Electrolysis** is used for these (see page 39). It is a very costly process because it uses a lot of energy. Less reactive metals can be extracted by cheaper methods such as reduction.

**Reduction** is a chemical reaction which involves taking away the oxygen (or other similar element) from a compound. Metals such as iron and lead are extracted using reduction.

Copper and mercury are extracted from their ores by **roasting them in air**. Some copper is found uncombined, but most copper is found in chalcopyrite (copper(I) sulphide, also called copper pyrites).

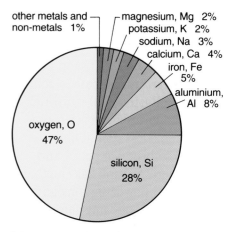

*Elements in the Earth's crust*

# Extracting aluminium

**Aluminium** is the most abundant metal in the Earth's crust, but one of the most expensive to extract. The main ore of aluminium is **bauxite**, which contains aluminium oxide ($Al_2O_3$), sand, and some iron oxide. The first stage in the extraction is the removal of the impurities, sand and iron oxide. The pure aluminium oxide left is called **alumina**, which melts at 2045 °C. It will not conduct electricity when solid, so to save heating it to this temperature it is dissolved in molten **cryolite** ($Na_3AlF_6$) at about 950 °C. This solution is a better conductor of electricity than molten alumina.

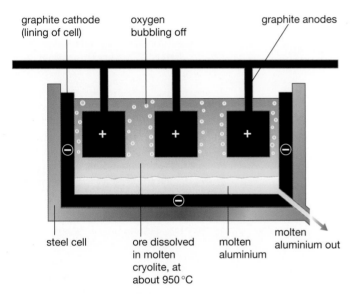

*The extraction of aluminium using electrolysis*

Electricity is passed through the alumina solution via electrodes. The electrode that is connected to the positive terminal is called the **anode**. The negative electrode is called the **cathode**. Both these electrodes are made of graphite. During electrolysis, the alumina is split up into its elements, aluminium and oxygen. Liquid aluminium collects at the negative electrode. Oxygen is released at the positive electrode. The liquid aluminium is siphoned off from time to time. Some of the oxygen reacts with the carbon electrodes to form carbon dioxide. This corrodes the electrode, which has to be replaced frequently.

## What happens during electrolysis?

Solid aluminium oxide does not conduct electricity. However, when it is dissolved in liquid cryolite, it does. Chemicals which conduct electricity are called **electrolytes**. To conduct electricity, a substance has to have charged particles which can move. These particles are called **ions**. Aluminium oxide contains positive aluminium ions and negative oxide ions. When aluminium oxide conducts electricity, the positive aluminium ions move towards the negative electrode. The negative oxide ions move towards the positive electrode. Each aluminium ion has three positive charges. At the negative electrode, the aluminium ions can take some negative charges (**electrons**) to cancel out this charge. The ions then become aluminium atoms.

$$\text{aluminium ions} + \text{electrons} \rightarrow \text{aluminium atoms}$$
$$2Al^{3+} + 6e^- \rightarrow 2Al$$

At the cathode, oxide ions give their electrons away.

$$\text{oxide ions} - \text{electrons} \rightarrow \text{oxygen molecules}$$
$$3O^{2-} - 6e^- \rightarrow 1\tfrac{1}{2}O_2$$

The whole process requires a great deal of electricity, which makes it very expensive.

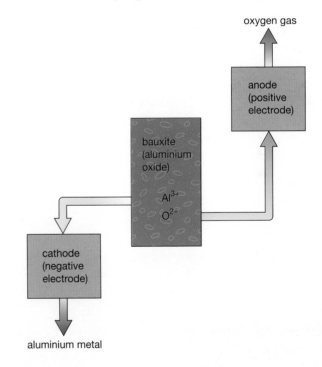

*Aluminium ions move to the cathode; Oxide ions move to the anode.*

## Questions

1  What is the main ore of aluminium?

2  Describe how aluminium is extracted from its ore.

3  Why is the aluminium ore dissolved in cryolite?

4  What happens at the cathode and anode during the electrolysis of aluminium ore?

# Uses of aluminium

Pure aluminium is a very reactive metal, much more reactive than iron, for example. However, if you try to react a piece of aluminium with dilute acid in the laboratory, it appears to be unreactive. This is because when pure aluminium is exposed to air it becomes coated with a very thin layer of aluminium oxide. This layer is almost transparent, and protects the aluminium underneath from further corrosion.

Aluminium is also a very strong metal, especially when alloyed with other metals (see page 45). Aluminium is a light metal with a relatively low density (steel is three times as dense). It is used to make light objects that need to last for a long time, for example aeroplanes. Its good conductivity of electricity makes aluminium useful for cables and wires in the electrical industry. The main restriction on the use of aluminium is its cost of production. It is possible to produce six times as much iron for the same cost. About 272 000 tonnes of aluminium are produced in the UK each year.

*The Thermit reaction in the laboratory (see Activity 3 below). Danger! This reaction is very violent.*

| construction | wall facings<br>roofing<br>windows and doors |
|---|---|
| transport | engines<br>superstructures of ships<br>aeroplanes |
| packaging | drinks cans<br>milk bottle tops<br>food containers<br>cooking foil |

*How aluminium is used*

*Aluminium has many uses. What properties of aluminium make it such a useful material?*

## Activities

**1** Gather together as many different objects as you can that are made from aluminium. Discuss their uses and decide what property of aluminium makes it suitable for each object. Display your findings on a poster.

**2** Find out the prices of aluminium, iron, gold, and zinc from a newspaper. Suggest reasons for their differences.

**3** Find out how aluminium is used to weld steels together in the Thermit process.

# Extracting iron

**Iron** is the second most abundant metal in the Earth's crust, and is the most used. The main ore of iron is called **haematite** and contains iron oxide, $Fe_2O_3$, and sand. The iron oxide is reduced (the oxygen is taken away) in a **blast furnace**. Over 700 million tonnes of iron are produced in this way each year.

The reactions that take place in the blast furnace are as follows:

- Coke (carbon) reacts with the oxygen in the air to make carbon dioxide.

  $$C + O_2 \rightarrow CO_2$$

- Limestone decomposes when heated to make calcium oxide and carbon dioxide.

  $$CaCO_3 \xrightarrow{\text{heat}} CaO + CO_2$$

- The carbon dioxide from these reactions reacts with more coke, making carbon monoxide.

  $$CO_2 + C \rightarrow 2CO$$

- The carbon monoxide reacts with the iron oxide. Liquid iron is made. This reaction is a reduction: the iron oxide is reduced to iron.

  $$\underset{\text{oxidized}}{\underbrace{3CO + \overbrace{Fe_2O_3 \rightarrow 2Fe}^{\text{reduced}} + 3CO_2}}$$

- The impurities, mainly sand, react with the calcium oxide to form calcium silicate or **slag**.

  $$CaO + SiO_2 \rightarrow CaSiO_3$$

The iron that is made in the blast furnace contains about 93% iron. This impure form of iron is called **pig iron**. Pig iron has very few uses because it is weak and brittle. Most of it is converted into **steel**. The slag is used for building roads. The blast furnace runs continuously. To save energy, the hot waste gases are used to heat the air going into the bottom of the furnace.

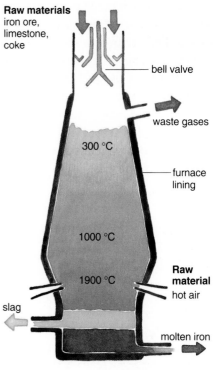

**Raw materials** iron ore, limestone, coke

bell valve

waste gases

300 °C

furnace lining

1000 °C

1900 °C

**Raw material** hot air

slag

molten iron

*The blast furnace – used for the extraction of iron*

*7000–8000 tonnes of iron a day are produced in the blast furnace.*

# Making steel

Most of the steel made today is manufactured in the **basic oxygen steel-making** (BOS) **furnace**. Steel is an alloy of iron. Different steels contain different amounts of iron. All steels contain some carbon which forms crystals of iron carbide. This strengthens the steel. The more carbon steel contains, the harder it is. However, adding carbon makes steel more brittle – to overcome this, the steel is heated and then allowed to cool. Sometimes other metals are added to the steel to change its properties.

| type of steel | contents (other than iron) | uses |
|---|---|---|
| soft | up to 0.15% carbon | sheets, wires |
| mild | 0.5% carbon | building (e.g. bridges), car bodies |
| hard | 1.0% carbon | hammers, cutting tools |
| stainless | 18% chromium, 8% nickel | cutlery, sinks |

The properties of steels can be altered by heating them in different ways. The table below shows the effects of heating and cooling steel in three different ways.

| treatment | properties |
|---|---|
| heat until red-hot, leave to cool very slowly | soft and easy to bend |
| heat until red-hot, cool by plunging into cold water | harder to bend, becomes brittle |
| heat until red-hot, cool in water, reheat, cool slowly | like original steel |

Cooling rapidly by plunging into water is called **quenching**. This freezes the structure of the steel in the high temperature form, which is hard and brittle. Reheating steel and cooling it slowly is called **tempering**. This returns the steel to its original form. The structure of iron crystals is different above and below 900 °C.

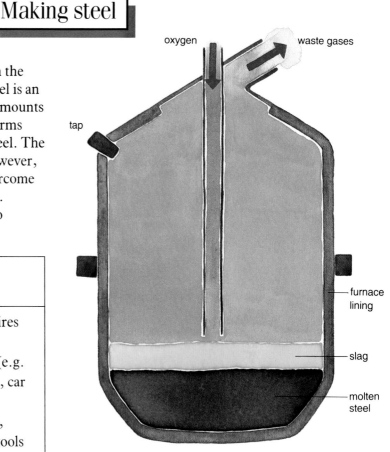

The basic oxygen furnace. Oxygen is blown on to molten pig iron. The carbon and sulphur present are converted to their oxides and leave the furnace as waste gases. The other impurities form **slag** which is skimmed off, leaving steel.

## Questions

**1** What are the raw materials used in the blast furnace?

**2** Write down the five chemical reactions that take place in the blast furnace.

**3** Why is limestone added to the furnace?

**4** What is the difference between pig iron and steel?

**5** Give five uses of steel.

**6** Where would the most economical site for a blast furnace be? Explain your answer.

## Activities

**1** Bend a piece of thick copper wire backwards and forwards. Does this change the properties of the copper? How do you think that this might be applied usefully in steel production?

**2** Pull a piece of copper wire using two pairs of pliers. (Wear safety spectacles.) Describe what happens.

**3** Look at a broken end of a piece of copper wire under a microscope and describe it.

# Extracting copper

Copper is less reactive than iron. Some copper is found uncombined in the Earth, but most is extracted from its ore, **chalcopyrite** or **copper pyrites** which contains copper sulphide, $Cu_2S$. The ore is roasted in air.

$$Cu_2S + O_2 \rightarrow Cu + SO_2$$

The copper obtained in this way contains about 3% impurities. To purify the copper, **electrolysis** is used.

The impure copper is used as the positive electrode, the anode. The cathode is made from a thin piece of very pure copper. The electrodes are dipped in a solution of copper sulphate. During the electrolysis, the anode dissolves and the cathode becomes coated in pure copper. The impurities sink to the bottom of the electrolysis tank. These impurities may contain small amounts of precious metals such as gold, silver, and platinum. These can be recovered and sold separately.

The ores that are mined today do not contain very large amounts of copper. The most economical way of mining copper ore is by **opencast mining** (mining from the Earth's surface). This destroys large amounts of the countryside, since it is not considered financially feasible to fill in the mine once it has been used. It is thought that our reserves of copper may run out within the next century.

## Electroplating

**Electroplating** is a process which coats an object with a metal layer using electrolysis. If a metal sheet is coated with a less reactive metal, this protects the sheet from rusting (see page 49). The object to be electroplated is used as the cathode in the electrolysis tank. The electrolyte that the electrodes are dipped in contains ions of the metal which will form the plating. The anode is also made of the plating metal. Some metals need to be plated with an intermediate metal before being plated with their final metal coating. For example, steel objects that need to be plated with chromium, such as car bumpers, have to be coated with nickel and copper, before being plated with chromium. The object to be electroplated has to be clean and free of grease.

Jewellery is often plated with gold or silver. Cutlery is sometimes coated with nickel and silver.

## Activities

1 Carry out a survey on the use of metal objects in the home, and what coatings (if any) they may have. Find as many metal objects as you can and try to find out what metal they are made of. Record your results in a table like the one below.

| object | use | metal | reason for choice | coating |
|---|---|---|---|---|
| knives and forks | eating | stainless steel | looks good, does not corrode | none |

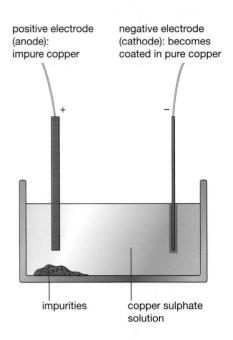

*Purifying copper using electrolysis*

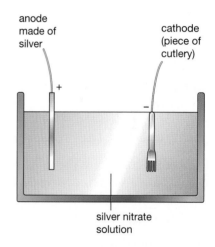

*Silver plating cutlery. The current must not be too large or the coating will not 'stick'.*

## Questions

1 What is the main ore of copper?

2 Give one reason why it is not necessary to extract copper from its ore using electrolysis.

3 Describe how copper is purified.

4 What is electroplating?

# Understanding the properties of metals

The general properties of metals are:

- High densities.

- High melting and boiling points.

- Good conductors of heat and electricity.

- Malleability (can be shaped by hammering).

- Ductility (can be drawn into a wire).

## High density

Most metals are much denser than non-metals. For example, the density of copper is about $9\,g/cm^3$ and that of gold about $20\,g/cm^3$! This is because the atoms are packed very closely together. The diagram shows how regular layers of atoms make up a large structure just like a crystal.

## Malleability and ductility

Although metals are dense and strong, they can be easily shaped by hammering. Metals such as copper can also be pulled into long, thin wires. This is because the forces we apply make the layers in the crystal slip over one another. The metal doesn't break, but it does change shape.

## Electrical and thermal conduction

When the metal atoms are close together, their outer electrons are able to move freely through the metal as a whole. We can think of the electrons as forming a 'sea' around the much larger positive ions.

When an electrical voltage, such as a battery, is connected to the metal, an electrical current flows because the electrons are free to move. Non-metals don't have a 'sea' of electrons in their structure so they do not conduct electricity. They are insulators.

The electrons in metal can also carry 'heat' as they move, so metals are good thermal conductors.

## Question

1   A cube of gold, 1 cm x 1 cm x 1 cm, has a mass of about 20 g. Find the mass of a 'rectangular' gold bar, 10 cm x 5 cm x 20 cm.
Comment on your answer.

*Atoms in metals are packed closely together.*

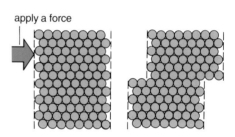

apply a force

*When a force is applied to a metal, the layers of atoms slip over each other.*

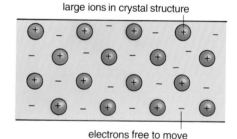

large ions in crystal structure

electrons free to move

*Electrons move around the metal ions.*

## Activity

1   Use a data book or other source to find the densities of:
   a)  iron, lead, silver, mercury
   b)  sulphur, bromine, oxygen
   c)  sodium, potassium.

2   Compare your answers for a) with those for b).

3   Compare your answers for a) with those for c).

44

# Alloys

The properties of a pure metal can be changed by mixing it with a small amount of another element. The different size of the 'new' element's atoms disrupts the regular pattern of the metal crystal. This can make metals harder and stronger. The new metal is called an **alloy**. The atoms which are added make it more difficult for the metal atoms to slip past one another, so alloys are usually less malleable and less ductile than pure metals. Alloys also tend to have lower melting and boiling points and are not such good conductors of electricity.

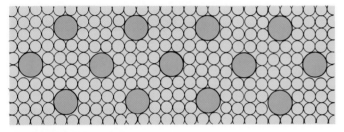

*Atoms in an alloy*

## Brass and bronze

**Brass** is an alloy made from a mixture of 60% copper and 40% zinc. It is much stronger than either of the metals on their own. Brass is very resistant to corrosion and conducts electricity well. It has many everyday uses including plumbing and electrical equipment, ships' propellers, and ornaments. **Bronze** contains 90% copper and 10% tin. It is used for statues.

*50p coins are made of 75% copper and 25% nickel. 2p coins are made of 97% copper, 2.5% zinc, and 0.5% nickel.*

*To make statues, molten bronze is poured into a mould and allowed to harden.*

## Solder

**Solder** is made by melting lead, which has a low melting point (328°C), and mixing it with molten tin. (Solder sometimes contains other metals.) Solder melts at an even lower temperature than pure lead. When it is solid, it is strong. These properties make solder useful for joining two pieces of metal together. Electrical wires can be joined together using solder.

*Solder melts at a low temperature. It can hold two metals together quite firmly.*

## Duralumin

Aluminium alloys are becoming increasingly important. The cost of aluminium alloys is high, but their properties make them very useful for making, for example, aircraft and window frames. The alloys contain about 4% copper plus very small amounts of other metals such as magnesium, silicon, and zinc. They are extremely resistant to corrosion, and are strong and light.

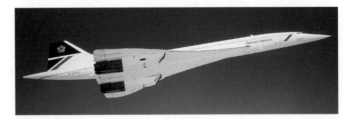

*Aluminium alloys are used to make aeroplanes.*

### Questions

1  What is an alloy?

2  Make a table with the following headings. Write in it all the alloys you can find out about.

| name of alloy | main elements | properties | uses |
|---|---|---|---|

# Reactions of metals (1)

Knowing about the chemical reactions of metals is important when working out how they can be used. For example, if a metal reacts with dilute acids, it cannot be made into a can for storing fruit, which produces natural acids. Similarly, metals that will be exposed to the air must not corrode too quickly.

## Metals with acids

When a metal reacts with a dilute acid, hydrogen gas is given off and a salt is formed. For example, magnesium reacts vigorously with the dilute acids used in the school laboratory.

magnesium + hydrochloric acid → magnesium chloride + hydrogen
(metal)       (acid)           (salt)

Some unreactive metals, for example gold, will not react with dilute acids. Others react slowly over many years. **Acid rain** attacks some metals and causes corrosion.

## Metals with water

Very reactive metals react violently with water. They give off hydrogen gas and form an alkali. For example, sodium reacts vigorously with cold water.

sodium + water → sodium hydroxide solution + hydrogen
(metal)            (alkali)

Metals which are less reactive, such as iron and zinc, react very slowly with cold water but react vigorously with steam. Unreactive metals, for example platinum, do not react with water or steam.

*Fruits contain natural acids which, although they are weak, will attack reactive metals.*

*These steel cans must be coated in the unreactive metal tin before they can be used to store fruit and other foods.*

| metal | symbol | reactivity with water | reactivity with dilute acids |
|---|---|---|---|
| potassium | K | React with cold water. | Violent reaction. |
| sodium | Na | | |
| calcium | Ca | Reactivity decreases going down table. | React. |
| magnesium | Mg | | Reactivity decreases going down table. |
| aluminium | Al | Protected by oxide. | |
| zinc | Zn | React with steam. | |
| iron | Fe | | |
| lead | Pb | No reaction with water or steam (lead reacts very slowly with steam). | No reaction. |
| copper | Cu | | |
| silver | Ag | | |
| platinum | Pt | | |
| gold | Au | | |

*Summary of reactions of metals with water and dilute acids.*

# Reactions of metals (2)

## Metals with air

Many metals react slowly with the oxygen in air. Moist air causes metals to slowly corrode. For example, iron reacts to form rust in damp air. However, reactive metals such as magnesium burn in oxygen. This is a fast reaction.

magnesium + oxygen → magnesium oxide<br>
(metal)                   (metal oxide)

If the metal oxide dissolves in water, it makes an alkaline solution. (If the oxide of a non-metal dissolves in water, it makes an acid solution.)

## Displacement reactions

When a reactive metal is placed in a solution containing ions of a less reactive metal, the less reactive metal is displaced from the solution. For example, if magnesium is placed in copper(II) sulphate solution, the magnesium dissolves and solid copper forms.

magnesium + copper(II) sulphate solution → copper + magnesium sulphate solution

We can use displacement reactions to investigate the reactivity of metals. Some results are shown in the table below.

*Aluminium, as used in these windows, reacts with oxygen to form a thin coat of aluminium oxide. This protects the metal from further corrosion.*

| metal | solution to which metal is added | | | | |
| --- | --- | --- | --- | --- | --- |
| | magnesium chloride | iron sulphate | lead nitrate | copper sulphate | silver nitrate |
| magnesium | ✗ | ⬇ | ⬇ | ⬇ | ⬇ |
| iron | ✗ | ✗ | ⬇ | ⬇ | ⬇ |
| lead | ✗ | ✗ | ✗ | ⬇ | ⬇ |
| copper | ✗ | ✗ | ✗ | ✗ | ⬇ |
| silver | ✗ | ✗ | ✗ | ✗ | ✗ |

⬇ Shows less reactive metal is displaced from solution.

✗ Shows that there is no reaction.

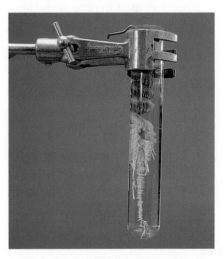

*Here copper has displaced silver from silver nitrate solution. You can see the crystals of silver.*

## Questions

1  An archaeologist finds some gold coins and some iron spearheads, which have been buried in the ground since Roman times. She washes them carefully. The coins shine brightly but the spearheads are a dull brown colour and their edges are rough. Explain these observations.

2  Sam is trying to identify unknown metal X. When he places it in copper(II) sulphate solution, there is a reaction and red-brown pieces of copper fall to the bottom of the test tube. When he places it in magnesium chloride solution, nothing happens.
    **a)** Give two suggestions for the identity of metal X.
    **b)** How could Sam find out which of these is the true identity of X?

# Rusting of iron

Iron and steel are among the most widely used materials in our society. This is because iron is one of the easiest and cheapest metals to extract from its ore. However, when iron and steel are exposed to the damp weather over a long period of time, they **rust**. During rusting, iron combines with oxygen to form a red powder called iron oxide, $Fe_2O_3.H_2O$. The rusting of iron and steel causes a great deal of damage, so it is very important to try to prevent rusting.

## Activities

**1** The conditions which cause rusting can be investigated by carrying out the following experiment and leaving it for a week or two.

- Place four clean iron nails into each of five test tubes. Label the test tubes **A**) to **E**).
- Leave test tube **A**) without a bung in.
- Half fill test tube **B**) with distilled water.
- Place boiled distilled water in test tube **C**) and pour on a thin layer of oil. This will float on the water and prevent any air from entering it. Put a bung in the top of the tube for extra protection from air.
- Dissolve some salt in water and add this to test tube **D**).
- Put some solid calcium chloride into test tube **E**) to take away any moisture from the air, and place a bung in the top.
- Record you results in a table with the following headings.

| test tube | appearance after two days | appearance after one week | appearance after two weeks |
|---|---|---|---|
| | | | |

- In which test tube did the nails rust the most?
- In which test tube did the nails rust the least?
- Under what conditions do iron and steel rust most?

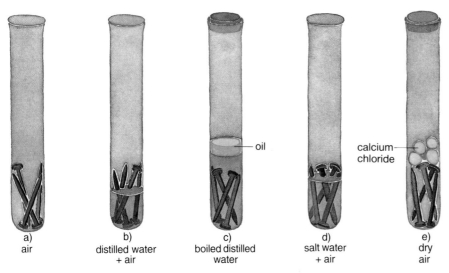

a) air
b) distilled water + air
c) boiled distilled water — oil
d) salt water + air
e) dry air — calcium chloride

*Experiment to investigate what causes rusting*

*Car manufacturers go to a lot of trouble to prevent this from happening too quickly.*

## Corrosion of other metals

Metals such as the reactive alkali metals (see page 27) corrode so easily in air that they are kept under oil for safety. Other metals are very resistant to corrosion – gold and silver are good examples. Not all corrosion of metals causes problems. Copper reacts with oxygen and carbon dioxide in the atmosphere and becomes coated in green **verdigris**. This protects the copper underneath from further attack. Aluminium reacts with oxygen to form a thin layer of aluminium oxide. This layer protects the aluminium from further corrosion in the same way. The aluminium oxide layer is made thicker if the aluminium is to be used for window frames. This is carried out using electrolysis and is called **anodizing**.

*Copper roofing with a coating of **verdigris**. What compound of copper do you think this is?*

# Preventing rusting

Many common objects in the modern world, such as motor cars, engineering tools, bridges, etc., are made from iron and steel. There are a number of relatively simple ways to protect these metals from corrosion. The method used depends on how much metal there is, and what the metal is used for. Some methods of protection are much cheaper than others.

Coating with grease or paint prevents air from reaching the metal. Large objects such as bridges and ships can be protected with paint. The paints that are used often contain lead or zinc, because these metals are good at preventing rust. Oiling bicycle chains at regular intervals helps to stop them rusting, and also ensures that they move freely. If a metal object needs to be protected from rust and look attractive, it can be coated in coloured plastic. Old gas and water pipes which are rusting can be coated inside with a new high density plastic.

*A protective coat of paint*

*What advantages does the plastic coating give to this furniture?*

*The gas board uses high-density plastics to line old gas pipes. This provides a relatively cheap method of replacing old pipes.*

Electroplating (see page 43) is used to coat cans that are used for storing food. The steel cans are coated with a thin layer of tin by electrolysis. Tin is used because it is non-toxic. If a can becomes dented, the protective layer of tin may become damaged and allow the acid from the fruit to react with the steel. Car bumpers, bicycle handlebars, taps, and kettles are all electroplated with chromium.

Iron sheds and dustbins are usually galvanized with zinc by immersing them in molten metal. They are coated with zinc because it is less likely to corrode than iron. Thirty per cent of all the zinc extracted from the Earth is used for galvanizing.

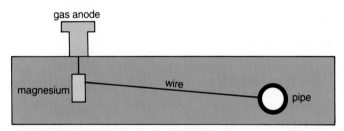

*Gas and water pipes can be protected from corroding using sacrificial protection.*

A more reactive metal can protect a less reactive metal in a method called **sacrificial protection**. Pieces of fairly reactive metals such as magnesium or zinc are 'sacrificed' to save such metals as iron or steel from rusting. Ships are protected by this method. A bar of magnesium is attached to the side of the ship under the water line. The magnesium corrodes before the less reactive iron. When the magnesium is used up, it is replaced. Underground gas and water pipes can be protected in a similar way.

## Questions

**1**  What conditions encourage rusting?

**2**  Rusting is oxidation. Explain this statement.

**3**  Name five different ways in which a metal can be prevented from corroding.

**4**  Why doesn't aluminium corrode easily?

**5**  How does sacrificial protection work?

## Activities

**1**  Find out how car manufacturers try to stop cars from rusting. Gather information by looking at various cars and from advertisements in newspapers and magazines.

# Chemicals from oil (1)

## Where is crude oil found?

Oil is made over millions of years by dead sea creatures being compressed. It is trapped by non-porous rock under the sea bed. Many reserves of oil have been found on the bed of the North Sea and **crude oil** is obtained from them by drilling. Crude oil is a thick, black, pungent liquid which is not very useful in its natural state. However, it can be split up into many useful products by **refining**. The crude oil is therefore transported to oil refineries on land.

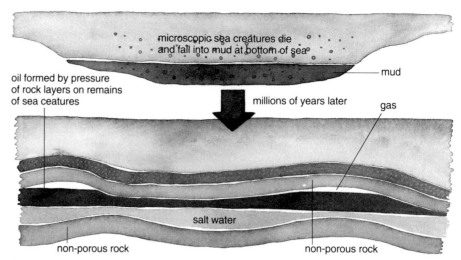

*Oil is formed on the sea bed from billions of sea creatures called **plankton**. They fall to the bottom of the sea and become trapped in mud. Millions of years later, other layers of rock have trapped the oil underneath non-porous rock.*

## What is crude oil?

It is a mixture of compounds called **hydrocarbons**. These are compounds containing only carbon and hydrogen. They belong to the **carbon** (carbon-based) group of compounds. The various hydrocarbons present in crude oil have different numbers of carbon atoms in their molecules. The carbon atoms are arranged in chains. Groups of hydrocarbons with similar length carbon chains are separated out from crude oil at an oil refinery.

### Questions

1  How was crude oil formed?

2  What is a hydrocarbon?

3  Crude oil is said to be a mixture of hydrocarbons. How is this mixture separated?

4  List the groups of hydrocarbons obtained from crude oil.

## Separating crude oil

Crude oil can be separated by **fractional distillation**. Each group of hydrocarbons has a different range of boiling points. As the oil is heated to about 500°C, gases are collected at different temperature ranges. This takes place continuously in a tall tower called a **fractionating column**. The groups of hydrocarbons are called **fractions**. The fractions with larger molecules (longer carbon chains) and higher boiling points are collected at the bottom of the fractionating column, and the fractions with smaller molecules at the top. The fractions are then refined further to produce chemicals that can be used.

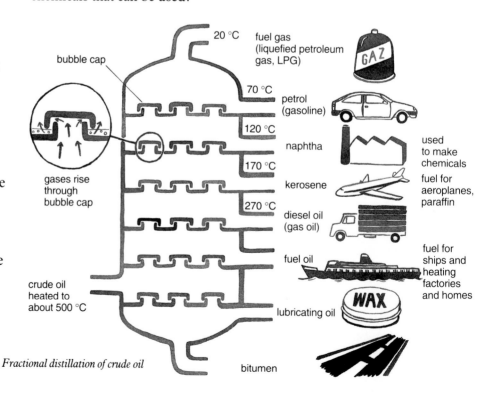

*Fractional distillation of crude oil*

# Chemicals from oil (2)

The fractional distillation of crude oil gives us important chemicals but it doesn't produce enough of some of the most useful hydrocarbons. We can make more of these by **cracking** the longer molecules into shorter ones.

Cracking involves heating the heavier fractions from the oil over a **catalyst** (see page 79). The catalyst helps the reaction to take place. The result is smaller hydrocarbon molecules, some of which contain a special **double bond**.

*We use a lot of petrol, so some oil is **cracked** to produce more of the useful alkane, **octane**.*

## Cracking

long-chain hydrocarbon

heated over a catalyst

alkane

double bond

alkene

## Alkanes

Alkanes are very useful as fuels. Some, for example butane and propane, are sold as 'bottled gas'. Others, such as octane, are used in petrol.

## Alkenes

Alkenes are very good for making other chemicals because the double bond makes them reactive. Used for making plastics such as polyethene, alcohol (ethanol), and antifreeze.

Some examples of alkanes and alkenes are given below.

| alkanes | | | alkenes | | |
|---|---|---|---|---|---|
| name | formula | | name | formula | |
| methane | $CH_4$ | | ethene | $C_2H_4$ | |
| ethane | $C_2H_6$ | | propene | $C_3H_6$ | |

# Plastics

Many objects that used to be made of metal are now made of **plastic**. One of the first plastics to be invented was celluloid. It was once used for making cine films, but it is flammable and caused very serious fires. It has now been replaced by cellulose acetate. In the 1940s many other plastics were manufactured.

*The list of uses of plastics is endless.*

A plastic is a synthetic material which can easily be shaped. Plastics are usually tough and versatile. They are very good electrical insulators. They can be spun into fibres to make clothes and carpets, or moulded to make objects such as cups or chairs. Plastics are **polymers**. Polymers contain very large molecules that are made by adding together many small molecules called **monomers**. (Poly means many, mono means single.) Some familiar polymers are polyethene (polythene), polystyrene, and poly(vinyl chloride) (PVC). The names of the corresponding monomers are ethene, styrene, and vinyl chloride. Nylon, Perspex, and Terylene are the common names of some other important plastics.

monomer

polymer

*Each monomer unit can be linked to the next to form one large polymer unit. This is similar to linking together a string of paperclips.*

## Addition polymerization

Addition polymers are made from alkenes. Alkenes are unsaturated organic compounds – they contain a double bond between two carbon atoms. When polymers are made from alkenes, the monomers 'add' to each other forming long chains of polymer. This is called an **addition reaction**. Alkenes are not found naturally – they are obtained by catalytic cracking of crude oil products.

*In polyethene each monomer unit is the same. It is like a string of beads all the same type connected together.*

## Condensation polymerization

Condensation polymers are made by reacting different monomers together. Usually a small molecule such as water or hydrogen chloride is also made during the process, which is called **condensation polymerization**. Nylon is made using this method.

*In nylon, the monomers are not all the same type. It is like a string of alternately coloured beads.*

## Activities

1   Make a list of all the plastic objects you come across in one day.

2   Collect information about different uses and types of plastics, relating the properties of each plastic to its use.

## Questions

1   Explain the words **plastic**, **monomer**, and **polymer**.

2   What is meant by **addition polymerization**?

3   How does condensation polymerization differ from addition polymerization?

# Polyethene and nylon

## Polyethene and nylon

**Polyethene** (**polythene**) is one of the most common plastics. It was first made in 1933 by heating molecules of ethene to a temperature of 200 °C at 2000 times atmospheric pressure. The product was an unstable white waxy solid which sometimes exploded! After some research, polyethene was made safer and was found to be a good electrical insulator. One type of polyethene can be made into thin transparent sheets that float on water. This is called **low-density polyethene**. However, it softens and loses its shape when heated, for example in boiling water. It is used for making food bags, washing-up bowls, and 'squeezy' bottles.

In 1953 a German chemist, Professor Ziegler, produced a variety of polyethene using a new method. Ethene was polymerized at atmospheric pressure using a catalyst. The resulting polyethene had slightly different properties. It did not soften when put into boiling water, was more rigid, and had a higher density. It is called **high-density polyethene**. Milk crates are made of high-density polyethene.

Polyethene is made by addition polymerization. The monomer is ethene. If high pressures and temperatures are used, low-density polyethene is made. At lower pressures and using a catalyst, high-density polyethene is produced. In both cases, long chains of about 50 000 ethene molecules added together are formed.

*Addition polymerization. Polyethene is made from the monomer ethene.*
n = *a very large number.*

## Nylon

**Nylon** is a plastic that can be made into thin fibres, which can be woven into cloth. Nylon is made by condensation polymerization. The two chemicals used have reactive 'ends'. When they join together, a small molecule – hydrogen chloride – is split off.

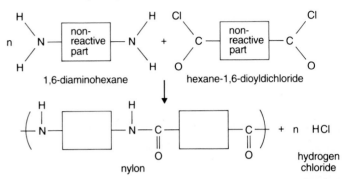

*Condensation polymerization. Two different monomers are joined together. Nylon is made by this reaction.*

Nylon can be made in the laboratory in the following way: hexane-1,6-dioyl dichloride is dissolved in an organic solvent, and 1,6-diaminohexane is dissolved in water. Both are poured carefully into a small beaker, and the two layers do not mix. Where the layers meet, the chemicals react to form nylon. If this nylon is slowly pulled out of the beaker, more nylon is formed. This is sometimes called the 'nylon rope trick'.

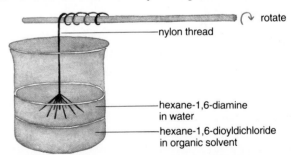

*In the 'nylon rope trick', the reaction only takes place where the two chemicals meet.*

## Questions

**1** Write a word equation to represent making polyethene.

**2** What is the difference between low-density polyethene and high-density polyethene?

**3** What two chemicals are used to make nylon in the laboratory?

**4** Why is the laboratory manufacture of nylon sometimes called the 'nylon rope trick'?

# Advantages and disadvantages of plastics

Plastics are synthetic (made, not natural). They have many advantages over natural materials such as wood, and other materials such as glass and metals. In recent years more and more use has been made of them.

## Advantages of plastics

- They do not rot.
- They do not corrode.
- They can insulate.
- They can be moulded into convenient shapes.
- They are generally light materials.
- Some plastics are very strong without being heavy.
- They can be coloured during manufacture.
- They can be very cheap to produce.

## Disadvantages of plastics

- They do not rot and so are difficult to dispose of.
- They give off poisonous fumes when burnt. (This is especially dangerous when foam furniture burns.)
- They are very cheap to produce compared with the cost of recycling them, so are usually thrown away.
- They often don't look as good as 'natural' materials.

Some of the advantages of plastics are also disadvantages. If plastics were more expensive to make, then we would think twice about using them so extensively. Since plastics don't rot, they can be used to make heart valves and other body parts. However, 5% of household waste is plastic. Most of the plastics we use are not biodegradable. It takes many thousands of years for a plastic yoghurt pot to disintegrate. Can you imagine how many yoghurt pots we get through in one year?

Plastics cannot easily be burnt because of the poisonous fumes which they give off. Plastics can be recycled, but at a large cost. If they were recycled, people would have to sort their rubbish into different types of plastic. This would take time and effort.

Scientists are trying to make goods out of **biodegradable plastics** which can be broken down by bacteria in the soil or by sunlight. There are some plastics today which do break down, but unfortunately they are not being used extensively. When oil runs out, plastics will become more expensive to make, so perhaps we will think more carefully about recycling them.

*Some of the more dangerous foam furniture is now banned.*

*Recycling plastics can be a problem. Making objects from degradable plastics is one way to reduce plastic pollution.*

## Activities

1  Do you think the advantages of plastics outweigh the disadvantages? Give reasons for your answer.

# Uses of plastics

How many uses for plastics can you add to the lists below?

| plastics | uses |
|---|---|
| polyethene | plastic bags<br>beakers<br>buckets<br>bowls<br>washing-up bottles<br>milk crates<br>dustbins |
| polystyrene | cups<br>packaging materials<br>ceiling tiles<br>ball-point pens<br>model construction kits<br>thermal insulation |
| polypropylene | washing-up bowls<br>carpets<br>string |
| poly (vinyl chloride), PVC | car seat covers<br>raincoats<br>records<br>hose pipes<br>curtain rails<br>electrical insulation |

| plastics | uses |
|---|---|
| poly (tetra-fluoroethene), PTFE | non-stick saucepans<br>soles of irons<br>bridge bearings<br>oven floors<br>plumbing tape |
| nylon | rope<br>brush bristles<br>tights<br>clothing |
| Terylene (polyester) | seat belts<br>yacht sails<br>clothing |
| melamine | unbreakable plates and mugs<br>work surfaces |
| phenolic resins | electric plugs<br>saucepan handles |
| Perspex | rulers<br>car windscreens<br>advertising signs<br>substitute for glass |
| Bakelite | electrical fittings |

*The contents of the dustbin provide an interesting insight to the use of materials in today's society.*

### Activities

**1** Carry out a survey of all the rubbish thrown away at home for a week. List the rubbish in different groups, such as plastics, paper, glass, metals and wood. What proportion of the rubbish is plastics?

Polyethene, nylon, and PVC are all **thermoplastics**. They become soft when they are heated. When they are cooled, they become hard again. They are also called thermosoftening plastics. They can be shaped when heated. It is possible to heat and cool thermoplastics again and again. Thermoplastics can be shaped in a number of ways.

## Extrusion

The plastic is heated to make it soft, and squeezed through a small hole. It is then cooled with cold air, which hardens it. Plastics to be made into long, thin strips are made in this way, for example garden hose pipes.

## Vacuum forming

Toys and baths are made by placing a sheet of plastic over a mould. The plastic is then heated and air sucked from between it and the cold mould.

## Injection moulding

Soft plastic is forced into a mould. After it has cooled, it is taken out of the mould. Dustbins and combs are made in this way.

## Blow moulding

This is similar to injection moulding, but the soft plastic is blown into a cold mould which is usually made of two halves. Plastic bottles and objects with complicated shapes are made like this.

## Elastomeric polymers

All rubbers are elastic. They can be pulled into different shapes, and return to their original shape afterwards. Natural rubber comes from the sap of the rubber tree. However, there is not enough natural rubber available for all needs. Synthetic rubber is a polymer made from an alkene called butadiene. Sulphur is added to the rubber to improve its elastic properties and strength. This is called **vulcanizing**. Vulcanized rubber is used to make tyres.

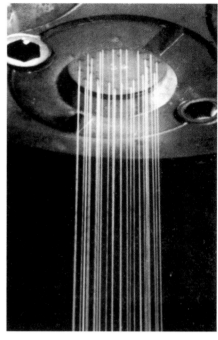

*Nylon fibres are made by extrusion.*

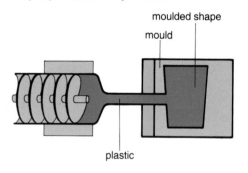

*Injection moulding*

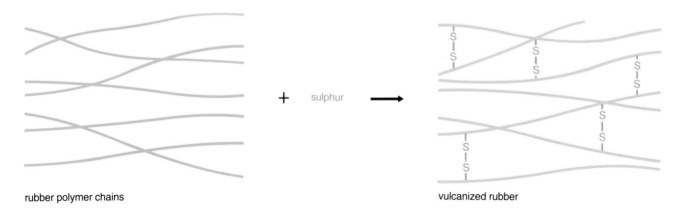

rubber polymer chains

vulcanized rubber

*When rubber is heated with sulphur, the polymer chains are linked together by sulphur atoms. The cross-links stop the polymer chains stretching.*

# Thermosetting plastics

Plastics that remain hard after heating are called **thermosetting plastics** or **thermosets**. If they are heated again, they do not soften so they cannot be remoulded. Examples include Bakelite, melamine, and glass reinforced plastic (GRP). Thermosetting plastics are usually very tough, rigid, and resistant to high temperatures. Melamine is often used for unbreakable plates and mugs. Bakelite was the first plastic to be manufactured and is very resistant to heat. It is used as an electrical insulator. GRP is glass mixed with polymers to make a light, strong material. It is used to make boats and canoes, roofing, piping, etc., since it also resists corrosion. There are two ways of shaping thermosetting plastics.

## Compression moulding

The plastic is heated and moulded at the same time, and compressed into shape.

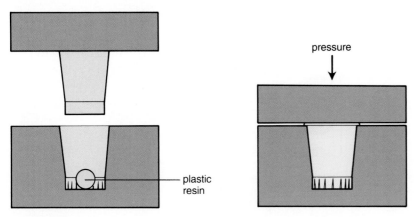

*Thermosetting plastics can be moulded using compression.*

## Lamination

Laminated plastics such as Formica are made by sandwiching layers of plastic with another material, such as paper or wood, and pressing them into thin sheets. This form of plastic is very heat resistant.

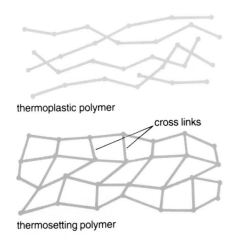

*The structures of a thermoplastic and a thermosetting polymer*

*Canoes made of GRP are light and strong.*

## Questions

**1** What is a thermoplastic?

**2** How do thermosetting plastics differ from thermoplastics?

**3** Explain, with the aid of a diagram, what extrusion is.

**4** Why can't Bakelite be extruded?

**5** Draw a diagram to show the difference in structure between a thermoplastic and a thermosetting plastic.

**6** Why is sulphur added to rubber? What is this process called?

Calcium carbonate, $CaCO_3$, is one of the most abundant minerals in the Earth's crust, second only to the group of silicates. There are different forms of calcium carbonate, namely **chalk**, **limestone**, and **marble**. Chalk was formed from the shells of dead sea animals and is a fairly soft material. Where it has been subjected to a great deal of pressure, it has turned to the harder form, limestone. Marble was formed by the effects of both pressure and heat on chalk. The most common of the three forms of calcium carbonate is limestone. It is used in the blast furnace for the extraction of iron (see page 41), and for neutralizing acid soil. Limestone is also used to make two very important materials – concrete and glass.

## Concrete

Many buildings and bridges are made of **concrete**. Concrete is a mixture of cement, sand, water, and gravel or small stones. Cement is made from limestone or chalk, depending which part of the country it is made in. Limestone is mixed with shale, while chalk is mixed with clay.

When added to water, the cement grows crystals which interlock with the sand and gravel, causing them to bind together. Using different sized pieces of stones, you can make different types of concrete. Mortar for bricklaying is made in a similar way, using a mixture of sand and cement.

Concrete is used in the building industry in many ways. It is often strengthened by pouring it over a framework of steel rods. This is called **reinforced concrete**.

## History of cement

The Egyptians used lime as a cementing material to build their pyramids. The Romans developed cement and made it stronger. In 1842 Joseph Aspidin patented Portland cement, which is still manufactured today. He called it Portland because he thought it looked like Portland stone. The cement was made in kilns shaped like beehives, which can still be seen in parts of the UK today. The chalk used to make (early) cement was mined by men with pickaxes, and then loaded into the kilns which were often kept burning for months. Cement made like this was used by Brunel to build a tunnel under the River Thames in 1838.

Many buildings are made of limestone. Limestones are fairly easy to cut and look very pleasant when they are slightly weathered in appearance. Normal weathering does not do much harm to the stones. However, since carbonates react with acid, buildings that are subjected to acid rain and a great deal of exhaust pollution from traffic can crumble and disintegrate over a number of years.

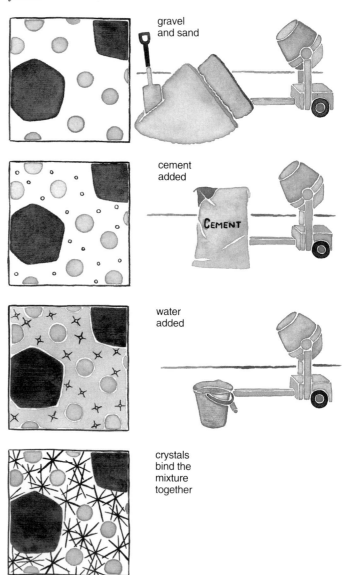

*How concrete and mortar are made*

## Questions

1  What are the main uses of limestone?

2  How were chalk, limestone, and marble made?

3  What are the starting materials for cement?

4  How is concrete made?

5  List as many different uses of concrete as you can.

## Glass

**Glass** is a very versatile material, also made from limestone. The raw materials for the manufacture of glass are sand (silicon dioxide, $SiO_2$), sodium carbonate, $Na_2CO_3$, and limestone. These three compounds are mixed together and heated to a temperature of 1500°C. The sand and sodium carbonate react together making sodium silicate, $Na_2SiO_3$. (This is called **water glass** since it dissolves in water.) The limestone helps to form a structure of calcium silicate and sodium silicate, which is not soluble in water.

$$SiO_2 + Na_2CO_3 \rightarrow Na_2SiO_3 + CO_2$$

Clean scrap glass called **cullet** is added to help the mixture melt. The cullet comes from glass containers that have been returned, such as medicine bottles, beer bottles, and chipped milk bottles. The glass can be coloured by adding small amounts of compounds such as iron compounds for brown glass, cobalt oxide for blue glass, and copper compounds for green glass. The most expensive red glasses contain gold!

## Making glass bottles

When the glass is at 1500°C it looks like treacle. It is drained from the furnace or tank and cut into large lumps called **gobs**. Each gob falls into a mould and compressed air is blown in to force the glass into a bottle shape. Throughout the process, the glass is kept hot – problems with stresses might develop if the glass were allowed to cool too rapidly. Milk bottles are coated with titanium oxide to prevent them from becoming too scratched.

*A ribbon of float glass being washed before it is automatically cut and stacked*

*Where is your nearest bottle bank?*

## Making float glass

The raw materials for **float glass** are sand (silica), soda ash, limestone, dolomite, saltcake, and cullet. These are fed into a furnace and melted at 1500°C. The molten glass formed is floated out as a continuous ribbon on a bath of tin. The surface of the tin is very smooth and, along with the high temperature, this makes the surface of the glass flat. Any irregularities are smoothed out. The glass is then cooled slowly and cut automatically, according to the customers' requirements. This type of glass is used for shop windows, cars, mirrors, and anywhere a distortion-free glass surface is required.

## History of glass

The Egyptians are thought to have been the first people to make glass objects. They coiled molten glass into jars and used them for oils and perfumes. Much later, glass bottles were made by blowing through a pipe with a lump of molten glass on its end. This is still carried out to make special objects, but the majority of today's glass products are made by machine.

### Questions

**1** What are the raw materials for the manufacture of glass?

**2** How is float glass made? What special property does it have?

# Composite materials

A **composite material** contains two or more types of material combined together to provide a 'new' material with different properties. One of the materials is usually a fibre. A composite material can be modified to give an object the properties desired. For example, reinforced concrete is much stronger than concrete on its own. Concrete alone is too brittle for bridges to support a large volume of traffic. By pouring the concrete over rods of steel, which act like fibres, the problem is overcome.

## Glass composites

Glass reinforced polyester (GRP) is made by mixing glass fibres with a polyester resin and adding a chemical hardener. The resulting plastic is very tough but very light. It is often used to make boats, since it is also very resistant to corrosion. Its other uses include piping, car body repairs, and roofing materials.

A layer of steel wire mesh can be sandwiched between two plates of glass, making the glass very tough. This is done as part of the rolling process during the manufacture of float glass. If a transparent mesh is used instead of the wire mesh, the reinforced glass can be used on the outside walls of a building.

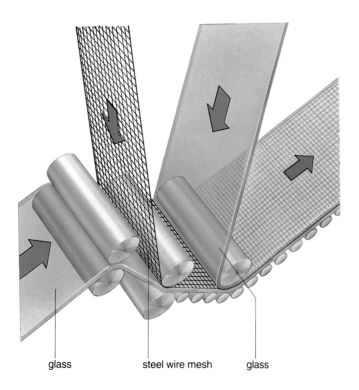

glass     steel wire mesh     glass

*Steel wire mesh can be welded in between sheets of glass to provide toughened glass.*

*Toughened glass is used in buildings to provide security and strength.*

## Graphite composites

Sports equipment is increasingly being made of graphite fibres. The fibres are very strong and are also very thin. Squash and tennis rackets are first made of an alloy with a low melting point. This is then dipped into a mixture of graphite in a plastic which sets very hard when heated. When the plastic has set, the alloy melts away leaving a very strong racket.

Plastics reinforced with carbon fibres are also used in the manufacture of Formula One racing car bodies.

*Graphite composites are used for sports equipment.*

### Activities

**1** Carry out a survey of either glass or graphite composites. Find out about their uses, their particular properties, and their manufacture. Write to different organizations and manufacturers for help. Present your findings in the form of a written report to the rest of the class.

About one tonne of rubbish is thrown away by the average UK home every year. The cost of disposing of all this waste is very high. It is possible to cover much of this cost by collecting and recycling as much waste as possible.

*Recycling would reduce the volume of rubbish to be disposed of.*

## What is the point of recycling?

Not all our natural resources are going to last forever. Minerals such as bauxite (aluminium ore) may run out in our lifetimes. Oil, which is used as a raw material for the manufacture of many plastics, is running out now. Scientists might discover new ways of producing aluminium and plastics without using these raw materials, or they may develop new, different materials to use in their place. However, we have the technology and the resources to reclaim many materials such as plastic and aluminium from our household rubbish now. Do you think we should recycle materials before it's too late?

## Glass

Glass is not biodegradable. The raw materials for the manufacture of glass are plentiful and relatively cheap to extract. However, the mining of both limestone and sand cause scarring of the landscape. Recycling glass would reduce this problem. Bottle banks are used increasingly in the UK to collect glass to make cullet. Producing new glass using cullet can save up to 25% of the energy costs during manufacture. By recycling glass we can also save on space in landfill sites.

*Glass needs to be disposed of safely.*

## Plastics

Since a great deal of our household rubbish is plastic, it may seem to be the best material to start recycling. However, there are many problems. There are about 30 different plastics in our rubbish, mainly in packaging materials. In order to recycle plastic, it has to be sorted out into these different types first. Who will do this sorting out? To make the recycling of large drinks bottles cost effective, 10 000 bottles would have to be collected to make just one tonne of plastic. Since the disposal of plastics is very difficult to carry out without damaging the environment (for example, burning them can give off toxic fumes), alternatives must be found. The search is on for a truly biodegradable plastic. A new polymer is being developed using sugar as a raw material. However, it is still cheaper to produce plastics from oil than from sugar! Other countries have made efforts to solve the problem. In some states of the USA companies can be charged a fine if they do not meet a recycling target each year. In Germany laws have been introduced so that a deposit is charged on all plastic bottles which are then returned to the shop. In Dublin a company uses unsorted plastics to make road signs for local authorities.

*Plastic waste can kill.*

61

## Oil

Waste oil can be re-refined to provide more fuel. Waste lubricating oil, used in car engines, contains up to 20% harmful additives. Used oil also contains more lead than new oil. Oil can be recovered from most waste oil, but at present only about 30% of waste oil is recycled. The rest is usually dumped down drains or burned. The pollution costs of this action are severe. Waste oil needs to be taken to certified recycling collection points. Do you know where your nearest one is?

*A small amount of crude oil can cause a great deal of pollution.*

## Costs of recycling

Whether to recycle or not depends on many factors.

- Is the material or mineral running out?
- Can it be recycled?
- If so, how can the material be collected?
- Does it cost more to recycle than to throw away?
- Should the cost only be considered in terms of money?
- What effects are there on the environment?

### Activities

**1** Choose one material and find out about how easy it is to recycle.

Find out about any local schemes in operation near where you live. Try and organize a collection of recyclable waste in your school.

## Metals

If a metal is expensive, then people think twice about throwing it away. The scrap industry recycles large amounts of metal every year. Fifty per cent of copper is recycled from pipes and old wiring, and 80% of the lead from car batteries is reclaimed. Producing pure copper from scrap copper only costs 3% as much as mining it.

*Scrapyards are full of a variety of metals. A large proportion of these metals can be separated and recycled.*

It is relatively easy to recycle large pieces of metal, but less easy to recycle metals which we throw away on a daily basis, such as drinks cans. Drinks cans are made from pure aluminium, or occasionally steel plated with tin. Both aluminium and tin are expensive to produce, so recycling them is worthwhile. Nearly all drinks cans are 100% aluminium. They can be separated out from 'tin' cans using a magnet – steel is magnetic, aluminium is not. Recycling aluminium not only saves bauxite, but also saves energy. Recycling needs only 5% of the energy used to produce aluminium from its ore. Different countries have different attitudes towards recycling cans. The problems are not usually concerned with the process of recycling, but rather with collecting the cans. In Denmark legislation was introduced which banned the sale of drinks in non-returnable containers. Charities can make money by organizing collections of cans for recycling.

*The mining of some raw materials, such as limestone or metal ores, can cause scarring of the landscape.*

# Case study: materials in cars

When Karl Benz built the first practical motor car in 1885, he used the materials that had traditionally been used to make horse-drawn carriages. As new materials have been developed, car manufacturers have used them to improve performance and safety.

*Benz's first petrol powered car, 1885*

## Metals

Most car bodies are made from steel. This is because it is cheap and easy to press into shape. The metal is treated and then painted to slow down rusting. At least one luxury car is made from aluminium – it will never rust!

Car engines must work at very high temperatures. Most are made from cast iron. This makes them heavy and reduces fuel efficiency. Some engines are made from aluminium alloy, which is much lighter.

## Synthetic materials

Modern synthetic materials are cheap and very hard-wearing. Seats are covered with material woven from synthetic fibres. Plastics are cheap, light, simple to mould and easy to keep clean. The dashboard and interior fittings can be made of plastic.

Plastic bumpers are lighter than chrome-plated steel bumpers and will not rust. They break in an accident, but can be easily replaced.

*Racing car bodies are made from composite materials, which include carbon fibres for strength. This makes them extremely light. At present, these composite materials are too expensive for use in ordinary cars.*

## Glass

*Car headlamps can now be made of hard, clear plastic rather than glass. However, windscreens are still made of glass, but it is specially treated and contains layers of plastic inside. This **lamination** makes it strong and prevents glass fragments from injuring people in an accident.*

### Activity

1 Look carefully at a modern car and list all the materials used in its manufacture.

2 Choose three different materials and give reasons why each was chosen for its purpose.

3 Which materials could be recycled from a car when it is finally scrapped?

**1 a)** Gold is mined as pieces (nuggets) of pure metal. Aluminium is found as the ore aluminium oxide (bauxite). Use the reactivity of the metals to explain why this is.
**b)** Suggest some experiments you could do in the laboratory to test your explanation.

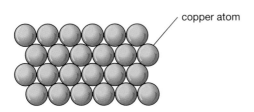

copper atom

**2 a)** The diagram represents the structure of copper. Use this model to explain why:
   i) copper is much denser than krypton although its atoms are smaller;
   ii) copper can be 'pulled' into long, thin wires.

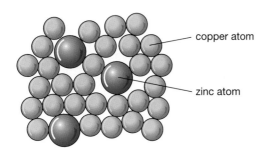

copper atom

zinc atom

**b)** This diagram represents the structure of the alloy bronze.
i) What is an alloy?
ii) How does the model help to explain why bronze is much harder to deform than pure copper?

**3** Using no more than fifteen words for each, give very brief details of how **a)** copper, **b)** iron, **c)** aluminium are extracted from their ores.

**4** Describe an experiment which could be used to test these hypotheses:
   **a)** Terry says that rust is caused when iron reacts with oxygen.
   **b)** Lucy says that rust is caused when iron reacts with water.
   **c)** Reshma says that iron only rusts when it is exposed to oxygen and water.

**5** The picture shows a can of fruit.

The can is made of steel coated with a thin layer of tin.
   **a)** Suggest why steel is a good material for making cans.
   **b)** Explain why the tin coating is necessary.

**6** The cans used for soft drinks and beer are made of aluminium.
   **a)** Suggest two reasons why aluminium is a good material for this purpose.
   **b)** Explain why it is important to recycle aluminium cans, even though supplies of aluminium ore are plentiful.

**7** The diagrams below show ethane and ethene.

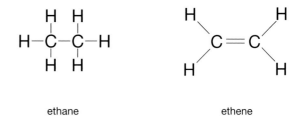

ethane                    ethene

**a)** Explain why ethene is much more reactive than ethane.
**b)** The plastic polyethene is made by the polymerization of ethene. Use a diagram to explain what is meant by **polymerization**.
**c)** Supermarkets give their customers plastic bags to carry their shopping. Give two advantages and two disadvantages of plastic bags, compared with paper bags.

*How can we tell what is happening in a reaction?*
*How fast is the reaction?*
*How far does the reaction go?*
*How can we make use of all this information?*

We are surrounded by chemical reactions: metals rust, plants grow and then die and decay, food cooks. Some chemical reactions are very fast, for example explosions, or very slow, for example buildings being eroded by acid rain. **In every chemical reaction a new substance is formed.** The new substance has very different properties from the starting substances.

*Some chemical reactions are very fast, others are slow.*

## Changes which are not chemical

No new chemical substances are made during a **physical change**. Physical changes are usually easy to reverse. Melting ice to form water is a physical change, and the water can be easily frozen back into ice.

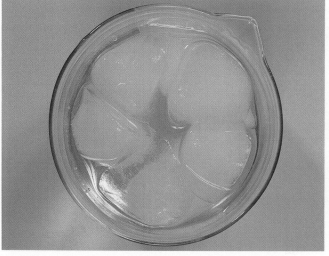

*When the ice has all melted, the water can easily be turned back into ice.*

65

The substances around us can exist in three forms: solid, liquid, and gas. We call these the three **physical states**. The photographs on this page show typical solids and liquids, and containers full of gas.

**Solids** have well-defined, rigid shapes. The crystalline solids shown have flat faces and sharp edges. Like all solids they keep their shape and do not flow over surfaces. Substances like sand and sugar may not appear to obey these rules but close observation shows that each 'grain' is a hard solid which behaves just like a larger crystal.

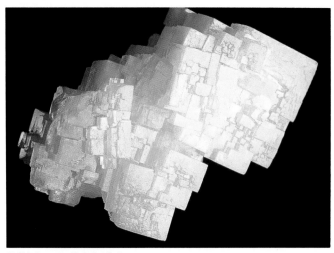

*Solids have well-defined shapes.*

**Liquids** do not have well-defined shapes and they flow. When a liquid is poured into a jar or bottle it takes up the shape of the container, but only up to a certain level. The liquid has a well-defined volume which can be measured using a measuring cylinder.

*Liquids take the shape of the container they are in but have a fixed volume.*

**Gases** do not have a well-defined shape. When a gas is placed in a container it quickly takes up any available space. Gases can also flow and it is possible to pour heavy gases from one container to another.

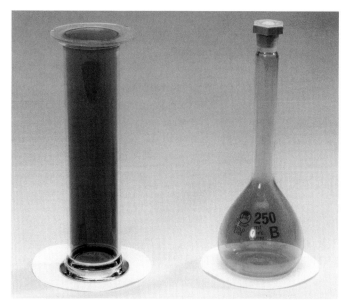

*Gases take up all the available space.*

Most materials can exist in all three physical states. Perhaps the best example is water. It comes out of the freezer as a solid (ice), out of the tap as a liquid, and out of a boiling kettle as a gas (steam). Heating or cooling water may change its state.

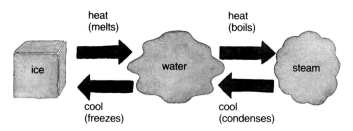

**The kinetic theory of matter** attempts to explain how solids, liquids, and gases behave. The theory is based on three assumptions:

- all matter is made up of tiny molecules or atoms which are continually in motion
- when the particles are close together there are attractive forces between them, and
- heating a material affects the movement of the particles.

# The kinetic theory of matter (2)

The kinetic theory explains the behaviour of solids, liquids, and gases in terms of moving particles. When these particles are close together they attract each other. This gives us the following models:

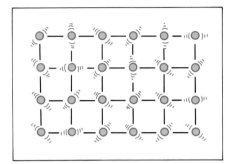

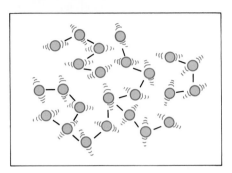

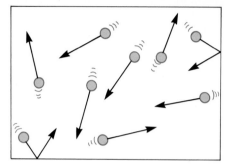

*In a **solid**, strong forces of attraction hold the atoms or molecules together in a regular grid or lattice. The particles vibrate but cannot break free. The solid has a fixed shape and volume.*

*In a **liquid**, the molecules are close together but they have enough energy to move about. As a result liquids can flow. At the surface the molecules attract one another forming a kind of skin above the liquid.*

*In a **gas**, the molecules are far apart and are moving so quickly that they do not really attract each other. They move in straight lines but have many collisions with other molecules and with the walls of the container they are in.*

We cannot see individual molecules in a solid, liquid, or gas. However, there is a lot of indirect evidence which makes us believe that they are constantly in motion.

## Diffusion

When the cap is taken off a bottle of strong perfume the smell gradually spreads out. After a few minutes it can be detected several metres away. We say that the perfume's vapour (gas) has **diffused**. This means that some of the molecules which were in the bottle have escaped and moved across the room. On the way, they have collided with the moving molecules in the air, so their progress has been rather slow.

Diffusion can also take place in liquids, as demonstrated by Activity 1 opposite.

## Brownian motion

We can get a better idea of molecular motion by looking at small particles of smoke suspended in air. A small glass cell is filled with smoke from a burning waxed straw. Through a microscope hundreds of bright specks can be seen. These are due to light reflecting from relatively large pieces of carbon and oil in the smoke.

If you look carefully you will see that these specks are moving in a jerky, zig-zagging motion. This is because the smoke particles are being bombarded by fast-moving molecules in the air. This random motion is

called **Brownian motion**. It is named after a Scottish scientist, Robert Brown. In 1827 Brown noticed that pollen grains moved jerkily when placed in water. In this case, the tiny pollen grains are being bombarded by fast-moving water molecules.

## Surface tension

Evidence that molecules attract each other can be found from looking at the surfaces of liquids. These behave as if they were covered with a thin elastic skin. This is because the molecules in the surface layer are attracted to the molecules in the liquid below them.

### Activities

**1** Take a glass Petri dish or a white saucer and fill it with water. Then carefully place one drop of ink from a pipette in the centre of the water. Do not stir the water. Watch as the ink particles gradually diffuse outwards.
Design an experiment to calculate the average speed of diffusion for ink into water.

**2** Fill a glass with water. Carefully add more water until the surface is above the rim. Sketch the top of the glass and the surface of the water. How does your diagram show that water molecules attract each other?

**3** Put a very thin layer of lard or butter on a small plate. Put two or three drops of water on the plate. Sketch the shape of each drop as seen from the top and the side. How does this show that water molecules attract each other?

# Molecular motion and temperature

A temperature scale gives us a simple way of comparing how hot objects are. The most commonly used temperature scale is the Celsius scale. The table below gives some common examples of temperatures on this scale. Notice that 0 °C is the temperature of melting ice and 100 °C is the temperature of boiling water.

| object | temperature |
| --- | --- |
| surface of Sun | 6000 °C |
| light bulb filament | 2500 °C |
| Bunsen flame | 1000 °C |
| boiling water | 100 °C |
| human body | 37 °C |
| summer day (UK) | 25 °C |
| melting ice | 0 °C |
| cold winter day (UK) | −10 °C |
| domestic deep freeze | −15 °C |

## What is temperature?

We have already seen that, according to the kinetic theory, molecules move more quickly when a substance is heated. The energy from the heat source is transferred to the molecules as increased kinetic energy. At the same time the substance's temperature goes up.

**We can think of temperature as a measure of the (average) kinetic energy of the molecules.**

We can now use kinetic energy to explain what happens when a hot object is placed in contact with a cold object.

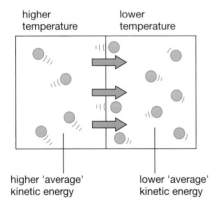

higher temperature        lower temperature

higher 'average' kinetic energy        lower 'average' kinetic energy

*Thermal energy always flows from hot objects to cooler ones.*

The hot object has many high-speed molecules. When these collide with the slower moving molecules in the cold object, they transfer some of their energy. The hot block gets slightly colder and the cold block gets slightly warmer. This goes on until eventually the two objects are at the same temperature. We say that they are then in **thermal equilibrium**.

When an object cools down its molecules slow down and have less kinetic energy. If we keep taking energy away the molecules will, in theory, stop moving! The temperature could never be lower because we could not take away any more energy. The lowest possible temperature is called **absolute zero**. Scientists have calculated this to be about −273 °C!

For scientific work it is convenient to use a temperature scale starting at absolute zero. The Kelvin scale starts at absolute zero and has degrees which are the same size as degrees on the Celsius scale. This makes conversions easy.

| Kelvin scale | Celsius scale |
| --- | --- |
| 1273 K | 1000 °C |
| 373 K | 100 °C |
| 273 K | 0 °C |
| 0 K | −273 °C |

## Questions

1 Explain the following using the kinetic theory:
   **a)** A spoon placed in a cup of hot tea gets hot.
   **b)** Adding cold milk to hot black coffee cools it down.
   **c)** A teapot should be heated with boiling water before tea is made in it.
   **d)** A kettle placed over a gas flame gets hot.

2 Convert the following temperatures to the Kelvin scale:
   **a)** 0 °C **b)** 100 °C **c)** 180 °C **d)** −173 °C
   **e)** −100 °C.

3 Convert the following temperatures to the Celsius scale:
   **a)** 0 K **b)** 73 K **c)** 150 K **d)** 473 K
   **e)** 561 K.

# Changing state

When a solid is heated it may reach a temperature at which it melts and turns into a liquid. According to the kinetic theory, the molecules in the solid get more energy as they are heated. Eventually they get enough energy to break free of the forces that hold them in place in the solid. If you keep heating, the liquid will boil and turn into a gas. This is because the molecules now have enough energy to break free completely.

### Activities

1  Fill a beaker almost to the top with crushed ice taken from a deep freeze. Quickly place a thermometer in the ice and record its temperature. Heat the beaker over a Bunsen burner and record the temperature of the ice/water every 30 seconds. Continue to do this until the water has been boiling for about 3 minutes. Plot the results on a graph.

The diagram below shows the general shape of the results graph. The four stages can be explained using the kinetic theory.

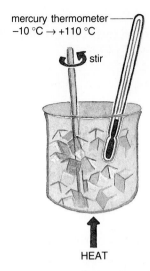

*Investigating the melting and boiling of water*

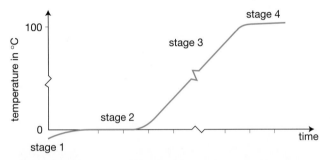

*When a solid melts or a liquid boils the temperature remains constant.*

**Stage 1**. Here the energy is raising the temperature of the ice up to 0 °C (melting point).

**Stage 2.** Here there is very little temperature rise. The energy is allowing molecules to break away from their fixed positions in the ice. The solid ice is turning to a liquid.

**Stage 3.** Here the energy is raising the temperature of the water up to 100 °C (boiling point).

**Stage 4.** Here there is no temperature rise. The energy is allowing molecules to break free completely. The liquid is changing to a gas.

## Specific heat and specific latent heat

The energy needed to raise the temperature of 1 kg of a solid, liquid, or gas by 1 °C is called the material's **specific heat**. The energy needed to melt 1 kg of solid without changing its temperature is called the material's **specific latent heat of fusion**. The energy needed to change that 1 kg of liquid into a gas at its boiling point is called the material's **specific latent heat of vaporization**.

The diagram opposite gives the values for water. Notice that we have to supply energy to melt a solid or to boil a liquid. However, when a gas condenses or a liquid freezes energy is given out.

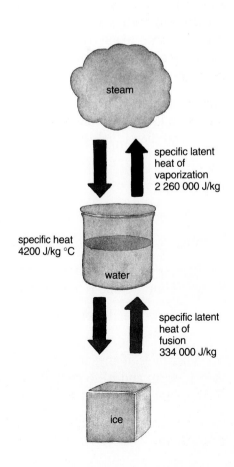

69

# Combustion and oxidation

When things burn in air they combine with oxygen: they are **oxidized**. The product of the reaction is an **oxide**. For example:

copper + oxygen → copper oxide

**Oxidation** means the addition of oxygen.

Many oxidation reactions produce hot gases, which can usually be seen as flames. These reactions are examples of **burning** or **combustion**.

When carbon is burnt, it is oxidized to carbon dioxide. You can see that energy is given out from this reaction in the form of heat and light.

Substances that can burn are called **fuels**. Most fuels are compounds of carbon and hydrogen (**hydrocarbons**). When they burn, they make carbon dioxide and water.

$$CH_4 + 2O_2 \rightarrow CO_2 + 2H_2O + \text{energy}$$

methane + oxygen → carbon dioxide + water + heat

Every day we make use of the combustion of fuels. The human body needs fuel to produce energy. Food is burnt up slowly, without any flames, inside the cells of the body. This form of combustion is called **respiration**.

We use fuels such as gas, coal and oil to heat our homes and produce electricity in power stations. Petrol and diesel fuels power our cars, buses and trucks.

*The fuel for this barbeque is carbon in the form of charcoal. It burns cleanly, producing a high temperature for cooking. A flammable liquid can be used to start the carbon burning. This provides the energy to start the reaction, which then gives out a lot of heat.*

*The fuel for this cooker is natural gas (methane). The products of burning methane are water and carbon dioxide. Methane is a clean fuel for use in homes.*

## Questions

1  What does oxidation mean?

2  What is produced when magnesium burns?

3  What is produced when a fuel such as butane burns? (Hint: butane is a hydrocarbon.)

4  Name two solid fuels, two liquid fuels and two gaseous fuels.

5  What fuels, if any, are burnt in your home **a**) to keep it warm and **b**) to cook food?
If your answer is 'none', explain why.

6  If someone in your family drives a car, what fuel does it use?

# Thermal decomposition

When blue copper(II) sulphate crystals are heated, water is driven off. White copper(II) sulphate powder is left behind.

A chemical reaction in which one substance splits up into two or more simpler substances, is called **decomposition**. The decomposition of blue copper(II) sulphate is caused by heating. It is an example of **thermal decomposition**. Thermal decomposition means 'breakdown on heating'.

Thermal decompositions are unusual reactions because there is only one substance to start with, but more than one substance is produced.

Some thermal decomposition reactions need lots of heat. For example calcium carbonate (chalk) can be decomposed by heating it in a kiln at about 800 °C.

The calcium carbonate is broken down into calcium oxide (quicklime) and carbon dioxide.

$$CaCO_3 \xrightarrow[800\,°C]{heat} CaO + CO_2$$

calcium carbonate → calcium oxide + carbon dioxide

Quicklime is used in making steel from iron, as a drying agent in some industrial processes, and in neutralizing acid soils.

## Questions

1 What does thermal decomposition mean?

2 Why are thermal decomposition reactions different to other chemical reactions?

3 Write down one example of thermal decomposition.

4 'When it is heated, zinc carbonate decomposes in the same way as calcium carbonate. Write a word equation for the thermal decomposition of zinc carbonate.

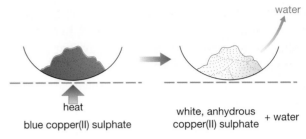

*Thermal decomposition of blue copper(II) sulphate.*

blue copper(II) sulphate — heat

white, anhydrous copper(II) sulphate + water

*This is a kiln for producing quicklime by the thermal decomposition of limestone.*

*Some plants, like these cabbages, grow better in neutral or slightly alkaline soils. Farmers use 'lime' to neutralize acid soils.*

# Reduction reactions

We have seen that oxidation is the addition of oxygen to a substance in a chemical reaction. When oxygen is taken away from a substance, we say that it has been **reduced**. **Reduction** is the removal of oxygen. Chemicals which reduce other chemicals are called **reducing agents**.

The diagram shows how black copper(II) oxide can be reduced by heating it in hydrogen gas.

The hydrogen takes the oxygen away from the copper oxide, leaving the red metal copper. The hydrogen is the reducing agent in this chemical reaction.

$$\text{CuO} + \text{H}_2 \rightarrow \text{Cu} + \text{H}_2\text{O}$$
$$\text{copper oxide} \quad \text{hydrogen} \quad \text{copper} \quad \text{water}$$

The copper(II) oxide has been reduced to copper. At the same time, the hydrogen **oxidizes** to water (hydrogen oxide). (The water passes out of the apparatus as steam.) The oxidizing agent is copper oxide, because it is the copper oxide that gives up its oxygen to the hydrogen.

Copper(II) oxide can also be reduced by carbon. When the two black powders are heated strongly, a reaction takes place. When the residue is washed, shiny specks of copper can be seen. The copper oxide has been reduced and the carbon has been oxidized.

We call chemical reactions like this **oxidation-reduction reactions** or, for short, **redox** reactions (**red**uction-**ox**idation).

## Questions

1  What does reduction mean?

2  What is a reducing agent?

3  What is the reducing agent in these chemical reactions?
   **a)**  aluminium + iron oxide → aluminium oxide + iron
   **b)**  carbon + copper oxide → carbon dioxide + copper

4  Where does the word 'redox' come from?

5  Explain why reduction and oxidation reactions occur at the same time. (Hint: use the two reactions in question 3 to help you in your answer.)

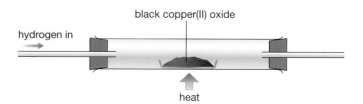

*Hydrogen gas passes over hot copper(II) oxide. A reaction takes place, leaving red copper metal in the tube. Steam (water) is also produced.*

*Here we can see that hydrogen has taken the oxygen atom from the copper oxide molecule.*

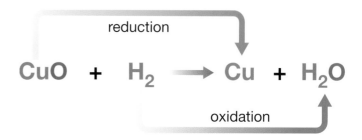

*Reduction and oxidation take place together in this redox reaction.*

*The redox reaction between aluminium and iron(III) oxide is very exothermic! Here it is being used to weld steel rails.*
$2Al + Fe_2O_3 \rightarrow Al_2O_3 + 2Fe$

# Precipitation

When two solutions are mixed together, an insoluble compound is sometimes formed. This solid product is called a **precipitate** and it usually settles at the bottom of the test tube or beaker.

For example, hard water contains dissolved calcium compounds such as calcium sulphate. To soften the water so that it will give a good lather with soap, we can add washing soda (sodium carbonate). A reaction takes place and insoluble calcium carbonate is precipitated or 'thrown out' of the solution.

The process is called **precipitation**.

$$Na_2CO_3 + CaSO_4 \rightarrow CaCO_3 + Na_2SO_4$$

| sodium carbonate | calcium sulphate | calcium carbonate | sodium sulphate |

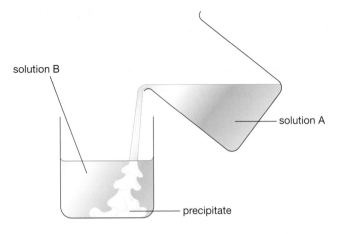

*When two liquids react to produce an insoluble product, we see a solid precipitate.*

## Another example

Barium chloride dissolves in water and so does sodium sulphate. When we mix the two solutions together, a reaction takes place, producing sodium chloride and barium sulphate. Sodium chloride is soluble and so stays in solution, but the barium sulphate is not. We see a white, solid precipitate form.

*The precipitation of barium sulphate.*

*Soap does not lather well in hard water. A precipitation reaction could help!*

## Questions

1  What is a precipitate?

2  Silver nitrate solution is mixed with a solution of common salt (sodium chloride).

| silver nitrate (soluble) | + | sodium chloride (soluble) | → | silver chloride (insoluble) | + | sodium nitrate (soluble) |

  **a**) Name the precipitate in this chemical reaction.
  **b**) Suggest how this precipitation reaction might be used as a test for 'chlorides'.

# Equations

There is an easy way of writing down what happens during a chemical reaction. It can be written as a **word equation**.

magnesium + hydrochloric acid → magnesium chloride + hydrogen

The **reactants** (left of arrow) are the chemicals at the beginning of the reaction. The **products** (right of arrow) are the chemicals that are made during the reaction. The arrow tells us that a reaction happens.

Word equations can only give a limited amount of information. **Chemical equations** are much more useful. A balanced chemical equation not only describes what chemicals are reacting to make other chemicals, but it also shows how many units of each chemical are involved.

zinc oxide + hydrochloric acid → zinc chloride + water

$$ZnO + 2HCl → ZnCl_2 + H_2O$$

This equation tells us that one unit of zinc oxide reacts with two units of hydrochloric acid to make one unit of zinc chloride and one unit of water.

## Rules for writing chemical equations

1  Write down the word equation.
2  Write down the correct formula for each of the chemicals.
3  Add up the atoms of each element on the left-hand side of the arrow.
4  Add up the atoms of each element on the right-hand side of the arrow.
5  If there are the same number of atoms of each element on the left-hand side of the arrow as there are on the right-hand side of the arrow, then the equation is **balanced**. If not, then balance the equation by putting numbers in front of the formulae.

## Example

Write a chemical equation for the reaction of magnesium with hydrochloric acid to form magnesium chloride and hydrogen.

**Step 1** Write a word equation:

magnesium + hydrochloric acid → magnesium chloride + hydrogen

**Step 2** Write in the correct formulae:

$$Mg + HCl → MgCl_2 + H_2$$

**Step 3** Add up the atoms of each element on each side of the arrow:

one magnesium,  one hydrogen,  one chlorine →
one magnesium,  two chlorines,  two hydrogens

**Step 4** Balance the equation.

The magnesium atoms are balanced. There is one either side of the arrow. The hydrogen atoms and the chlorine atoms are not. We need more of both on the left-hand side. If we put a 2 in front of the hydrochloric acid, the equation balances.

**Balanced equation:**

$$Mg + 2HCl → MgCl_2 + H_2$$

*This is what we see when magnesium reacts with hydrochloric acid. We can describe the changes by writing a word equation. We can give even more detail in a chemical equation.*

## Questions

1  Which of the following equations is balanced?

**a)** $Zn + HCl → ZnCl_2 + H_2$

**b)** $Na_2CO_3 + H_2SO_4 →$
$Na_2SO_4 + H_2O + CO_2$

**c)** $K + Cl_2 → KCl$

**d)** $CaCO_3 → CaO + CO_2$

**e)** $Al + O_2 → Al_2O_3$

2  Write down those equations in question 1 that are not balanced, and try to balance them.

# Rate of chemical change

Some chemical reactions are very fast. They only take fractions of a second to happen. Explosions are very fast reactions. Other chemical reactions, such as the ripening of fruit, can take days or even months. The **rate** at which chemical reactions take place can be measured very accurately. In industry it is very important to be able to make a substance in the most economical time possible. There are many different ways in which the rate of reaction can be controlled.

*Explosives can be used destructively.*

## What is the rate?

We measure how fast we are travelling in a car by looking at the speedometer. If it tells us that we are going at a speed of 70 km/h, then in one hour we will travel 70 km.

In chemical reactions we use **rate of reaction** to tell us how fast a chemical reaction is happening.

$$\text{rate of chemical reaction} = \frac{\text{change in amount of a substance}}{\text{time}}$$

The change in amount of substance measured can be the amount of product formed or the amount of reactant used up, the change in volume, pressure, conductivity, or colour, with time. For example, if a reaction involves the formation of a substance that has a colour, and all the other chemicals involved are colourless, then the rate of the reaction can be followed by measuring how long it takes for the colour to appear.

*Tomatoes take a few weeks to ripen – the reaction is controlled by chemicals in the fruit.*

## Measuring the rate of a chemical reaction

The rate of reaction of calcium carbonate with dilute hydrochloric acid can be measured using the apparatus shown below.

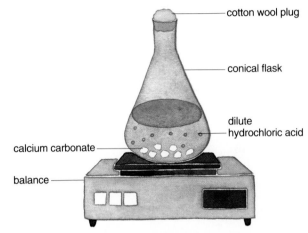

- cotton wool plug
- conical flask
- dilute hydrochloric acid
- calcium carbonate
- balance

*The decrease in mass during the experiment is noted at one-minute intervals.*

| calcium carbonate | + | hydrochloric acid | → | calcium chloride | + | carbon dioxide | + | water |
|---|---|---|---|---|---|---|---|---|
| $CaCO_3$ | + | $2HCl$ | → | $CaCl_2$ | + | $CO_2$ | + | $H_2O$ |

During the reaction carbon dioxide gas is given off, causing a reduction in mass. The cotton wool is placed in the mouth of the conical flask to prevent any liquid escaping, but at the same time allowing the carbon dioxide gas to escape. The results of such an experiment are plotted on the graph.

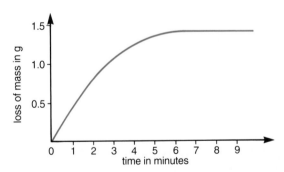

## Questions

**1** Look at the graph (above) showing the loss in mass during the reaction of calcium carbonate with hydrochloric acid.

**a)** What mass of carbon dioxide has been lost from the flask after i) 2 minutes   ii) 4 minutes?

**b)** What is happening to the rate of reaction as time goes on?

**c)** Why does the graph become horizontal after 7 minutes?

# Changing the rate (1): area

For a chemical reaction to happen, particles must come into contact with each other. To speed up a chemical reaction you need to increase the chance of particles colliding with each other. This can be done in four different ways:

- increasing the surface area
- altering the concentration (or pressure for gaseous reactions)
- altering the temperature
- using a catalyst.

## Surface area

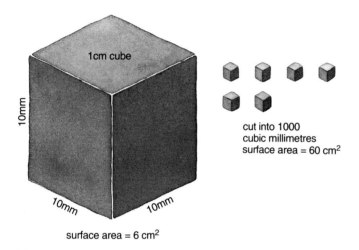

surface area = 6 cm²

cut into 1000 cubic millimetres surface area = 60 cm²

*The smaller the particles, the larger the surface area.*

When a solid reacts with a liquid, the reaction can only happen on the surface of the solid. This is the only place where the particles have a chance to collide. If the surface area of the solid is increased, then the chance for collision is increased. More collisions means more reactions between particles. This results in a quicker reaction.

The reaction between calcium carbonate and dilute hydrochloric acid can be used to investigate the effect of surface area on reaction rate.

### Example

20 g of large calcium carbonate chips were reacted with 50 cm³ of dilute hydrochloric acid using the apparatus in the diagram on page 75. The loss in mass was noted every minute. (Experiment 1)

The experiment was repeated using 20 g of calcium carbonate in small pieces. The results from both experiments were put in a table. (Experiment 2)

| time in minutes | experiment 1 loss in mass in g | experiment 2 loss in mass in g |
|---|---|---|
| 1 | 1.20 | 2.20 |
| 2 | 2.00 | 3.10 |
| 3 | 2.60 | 3.50 |
| 4 | 3.00 | 3.70 |
| 5 | 3.30 | 3.80 |
| 6 | 3.50 | 3.80 |
| 7 | 3.65 | 3.80 |
| 8 | 3.75 | 3.80 |
| 9 | 3.80 | 3.80 |
| 10 | 3.80 | 3.80 |

## Questions

1  Plot a graph of loss in mass against time for the reaction with the large chips.

2  On the same graph plot the results of the experiment with the small chips.

3  Which experiment has the fastest rate at the start of the reaction?

4  Why do both graphs become horizontal eventually?

5  What does the graph tell you about the effect of surface area on the rate of reaction?

6  Why was cotton wool placed in the tops of the flasks?

7  When there was no more gas given off, some unreacted calcium carbonate was left in the flask in both experiments. Why?

## Activities

These investigations can be carried out at home.

1  Measure out a mass of sea salt and add it to a cup of water at room temperature. Make a note of how fast it appears to dissolve without stirring the solution.

Repeat the same experiment using the same mass of table salt and then crushed sea salt. Which dissolves fastest? Why?

2  Carry out a similar investigation using stock cubes or sugar cubes.

# Changing the rate (2): concentration

If the **concentration** of a solution is increased, then the number of particles in a given volume of the solution is increased. The more particles there are, the greater the chance of particles colliding. The rate of reaction will increase.

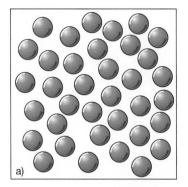 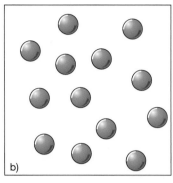

*The more particles there are, the greater the chance of collision.*

*In the early morning there are few people on this beach . . .*

When magnesium reacts with dilute hydrochloric acid, hydrogen gas is given off. The rate of the reaction can be measured by collecting the gas using the apparatus shown in the diagram.

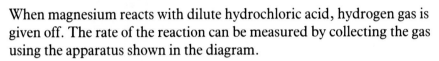

magnesium + hydrochloric acid → magnesium chloride + hydrogen

$$Mg + 2HCl \rightarrow MgCl_2 + H_2$$

To start the reaction the flask is tilted and the tube falls over. The magnesium then starts to react with the acid. The gas is collected in a gas syringe. The volume of gas given off is noted every half minute. The results of two experiments carried out with two different concentrations of acid are plotted on the graph.

*. . . collisions are much more likely later in the day.*

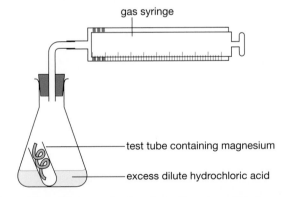

*Apparatus used for measuring the volume of gas given off during a reaction*

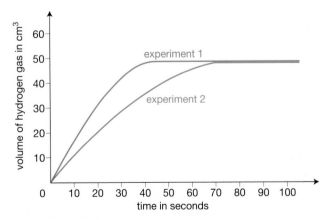

## Questions

**1**  Which experiment used the more concentrated acid? (see fig right).

**2**  At about what time would the reaction be over if the concentration of acid was twice that of the acid used in experiment 1?

**3**  Why is it important to use the same mass of magnesium in each experiment?

## Gas reactions

It is possible to increase the concentration of a gas by increasing the **pressure**. Some industrial processes are carried out at high pressures to help speed the reaction up. In the Haber process, nitrogen and hydrogen gases react to make ammonia gas (see page 86) and high pressures are used during the reaction.

# Changing the rate (3): temperature

Bread turns mouldy fairly quickly if it is left in a warm place. However, if it is in a freezer or even in a fridge it keeps fresh for much longer. Many foods are frozen to store them for long periods of time. Generally, chemical reactions go faster if the temperature is increased.

When the temperature of a reaction is increased the particles are given more energy When they have more energy they move about much faster. If the particles move faster and collide with more energy, then they are more likely to react with each other.

## An experiment to investigate the effect of temperature on a reaction

When 50 cm³ of weak sodium thiosulphate solution reacts with 5 cm³ of dilute hydrochloric acid a cloudy precipitate of sulphur appears. As the reaction proceeds, more sulphur is precipitated. The cloudiness becomes thicker.

$$Na_2S_2O_3(aq) \; + \; 2HCl(aq) \; \rightarrow \; 2NaCl(aq) \; + \; H_2O(l) \; + \; S(s) \; + \; SO_2(g)$$

The rate of this reaction can be studied by putting a cross on a piece of paper and carrying out the reaction in a flask placed on this paper. The reaction is viewed from above and the time taken for the precipitate to make the cross 'disappear'. The results of experiments at different temperatures are given in the table below.

look down at cross ▮ at beginning of reaction

clear

unable to see cross ▮ at end of reaction

cloudy

*The flask is placed on a piece of paper with a cross drawn on it. The time taken for the cross to disappear is taken as the time for the reaction to reach an end.*

| temperature in °C | time taken for cross to disappear (in seconds) |
|---|---|
| 25 | 120 |
| 30 | 80 |
| 35 | 60 |
| 50 | 25 |
| 60 | 20 |

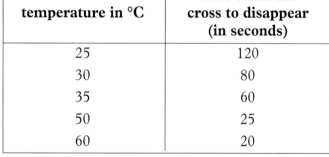

*Why do you think food lasts much longer in a fridge, especially during hot weather?*

## Questions

These questions refer to the experiment using sodium thiosulphate.

**1** If the temperature of the reaction is increased by 10 °C how does this affect the rate of the reaction?

**2** Plot the results on a graph (temperature on the horizontal axis) and estimate the time it would take for the cross to disappear at 40 °C.

**3** Copy and complete the following sentence:

'The rate of a chemical reaction _____ when the _____ is raised.'

**4** Describe how you could investigate the effect of concentration on reaction rate using this chemical reaction.

## Activities

You can carry out this experiment at home, using Alka-Seltzer tablets and water.

**1** Investigate the effect of surface area on the dissolving of an Alka-Seltzer tablet. Remember to keep the volume and temperature constant for each experiment. Try the experiment with one whole tablet first. Cut another tablet into four pieces for the second experiment, and crush up a tablet for the final experiment.

Design an experiment to investigate the effect of temperature on the rate of a chemical reaction using Alka-Seltzer tablets as before.

# Changing the rate (4): catalysts

Another way to alter the rate of a chemical reaction is to use a catalyst. This is a chemical that changes the rate of a reaction without being used up itself. Catalysts are used very extensively in the industrial production of ammonia and sulphuric acid (see pages 82 and 83). Our bodies contain catalysts. These are called enzymes or biological catalysts. Liver contains an enzyme, catalase, which decomposes hydrogen peroxide in the body.

## How catalysts work

When molecules collide they will only react if they have enough energy. Catalysts can help reactions happen at a much lower energy than usual. The reaction speeds up without increasing the temperature or concentration. Using catalysts saves industry a great deal of money. However, catalysts usually need to be of a very high quality and are themselves expensive to produce.

*Checking a platinum-rhodium catalyst gauze used in the production of nitric acid by oxidation of ammonia*

*Catalytic converters are fitted as standard on cars in the USA. Unfortunately, they do not remove carbon dioxide from the exhaust gases. Carbon dioxide contributes to the greenhouse effect.*

## Activities

1   Some washing powders contain biological catalysts (enzymes) that help remove biological stains. Design and carry out an experiment to compare the stain-removing powers of biological and non-biological washing powders.

2   Find out how enzymes are used in the production of beer.

## Uses of catalysts

Transition metals and their compounds are used extensively as catalysts. Nickel is used to speed up the change of vegetable oils into solid margarine. Vanadium(V) oxide is used in the manufacture of sulphuric acid. Iron is used in the Haber process for the manufacture of ammonia.

Biological catalysts are used increasingly in industry. Enzymes are used in the manufacture of beer, yoghurt, fruit juices, cheese, and in the pharmaceutical industry.

The harmful polluting gases that are emitted from a car exhaust can be converted into less harmful gases by a **catalytic converter** fitted to the car's exhaust system. These have been fitted to every new car in the USA since 1981. They help reduce harmful nitrogen oxides to nitrogen.

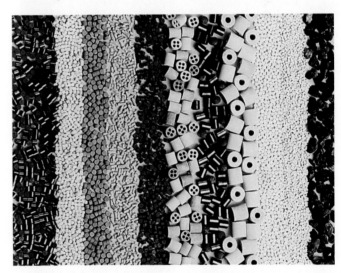

*The catalysts used in industry are made in a variety of shapes and sizes. Using small, cylindrical 'pellets' or fine gauzes increases the surface area where reactions can take place. The catalyst does not get used up in the reaction but impurities build up on the surface. Eventually the catalyst stops working and has to be replaced.*

## Questions

1   What is a catalyst?

2   Give two examples of catalysts and their uses.

3   What is an enzyme?

4   List the four ways in which the rate of a chemical reaction can be changed.

Frying an egg is a one-way reaction. Once the egg has been fried it is impossible to change it back into a raw egg. The burning of fuel is another one-way reaction. Many chemical reactions are of this type. Reactions which are one way are called **irreversible reactions**.

*Cooking eggs is not a reversible reaction.*

## Reversible reactions

There are some changes which can be reversed. A simple example is the physical change when ice is heated to form water. The water can be changed back into ice. The change can be written as an equation.

$$H_2O(s) \underset{\text{freeze}}{\overset{\text{heat}}{\rightleftarrows}} H_2O(l)$$

Another reversible change is the heating of blue (hydrated) copper sulphate. It decomposes to give white (anhydrous) copper sulphate and water vapour.

$$CuSO_4.5H_2O(s) \overset{\text{heat}}{\rightarrow} CuSO_4(s) + 5H_2O(g)$$

If water is added to the white copper sulphate the reaction is reversed. Blue copper sulphate is reformed and thermal energy is released.

$$CuSO_4(s) + 5H_2O(l) \rightarrow CuSO_4.5H_2O(s)$$

The whole process can be written down in one equation.

$$\underset{\text{blue}}{CuSO_4.5H_2O(s)} \overset{\text{heat}}{\rightleftarrows} \underset{\text{white}}{CuSO_4(s)} + 5H_2O(l)$$

This is called a **reversible reaction**. The symbol for this is $\rightleftarrows$.

## Reactions in equilibrium

When a mixture of water and ice is kept at 0 °C there is a **balance** of ice and (liquid) water. If we do not add or take away thermal energy, the amount of each will stay the same. In some chemical reactions the reactants and products are present together and the reaction seem to stop. These reactions are in **equilibrium**.

*Icebergs are in equilibrium with the water around them. If the temperature is increased, then more ice melts into water. If the temperature is decreased, then the process is reversed. Holes in the ozone layer can cause icebergs to melt.*

Someone walking up an escalator which is moving downwards may appear to stay in the same place. However, both the escalator and the person are moving at the same speed. They are in **equilibrium**.

*The person and the escalator are both moving, but their relative positions do not change. This is a dynamic equilibrium.*

An equilibrium reaction is a reversible reaction in which neither the forward reaction nor the backward reaction is complete. The symbol for equilibrium is $\rightleftarrows$. Therefore at 0°C the 'reaction' between water and ice can be written as an equation.

$$H_2O(s) \rightleftarrows H_2O(l)$$

# Equilibrium (2)

## Equilibrium reactions

When ammonia gas and hydrogen chloride gas come into contact with each other, a white cloud of ammonium chloride is formed. If solid ammonium chloride is heated it decomposes to give ammonia gas and hydrogen chloride gas. Under certain conditions this reversible reaction becomes an equilibrium reaction.

$$NH_4Cl(s) \rightleftharpoons NH_3(g) + HCl(g)$$

If solid ammonium chloride is heated in a sealed flask an equilibrium reaction is set up. When the gases are formed they cannot escape and so are able to reform ammonium chloride. Both reactions are happening at the same time. This is called **dynamic equilibrium**.

Many different industries make use of equilibrium reactions. The manufacture of ammonia and sulphuric acid both involve equilibrium reactions. There is an important equilibrium reaction going on in our bodies all the time. Chemicals in our blood, called **buffers**, help keep the pH of blood at 7.4. This is important since a change of pH of just 0.5 units can be fatal.

ammonium chloride

*When ammonia and hydrogen chloride gases come into contact, white fumes of ammonium chloride are seen.*

## Changing the position of equilibrium

**Concentration**: When extra reactant is added to an equilibrium reaction, more product is formed. Adding more product will produce more reactant.

**Temperature**: If the energy needed to break chemical bonds is greater than the energy released in forming new bonds, then the reaction takes in heat. This type of reaction is called an **endothermic** reaction. Increasing the temperature helps this type of reaction. For example:

$$N_2O_4(g) \overset{heat}{\rightleftharpoons} 2NO_2(g)$$

In this reaction, the formation of $NO_2$ is an endothermic reaction. So by increasing the temperature, more $N_2O_4$ is changed into $NO_2$.

**Pressure**: In reactions where the reactants and products are gases, increasing the pressure speeds up the reaction which is forming fewer molecules. In the example above, increasing the pressure would speed up the reaction where two molecules of $NO_2$ form one molecule of $N_2O_4$.

**Catalysts**: These do not affect the position of the equilibrium, but they do allow equilibrium to be reached much more quickly.

### Questions

**1** What is meant by **reversible reaction** and **dynamic equilibrium**?

**2** The heating of purple hydrated cobalt chloride, $CoCl_2.6H_2O$, is a reversible reaction. Blue anhydrous cobalt chloride is formed. Write an equation to represent this reaction.

**3** Give two examples of a dynamic equilibrium.

**4** How do temperature and concentration affect equilibrium?

# Rate of reaction in industry

In many industrial processes it is important to produce a chemical as cheaply and quickly as possible. Concentration of chemicals, temperature of reaction, pressure, and the use of catalysts are all factors in the efficient production of a chemical.

Two important industrial processes are the **Haber process** for the manufacture of ammonia, and the **Contact process** for the manufacture of sulphuric acid.

## Ammonia

85 million tonnes of ammonia are manufactured in the world each year. About 80% of the ammonia produced is used to make fertilizers such as ammonium sulphate, ammonium nitrate, and urea. The remainder is used to make nitric acid, nylon, and other chemicals.

## The Haber process

In the early nineteenth century a German chemist called **Fritz Haber** solved the problem of how to make ammonia on a large commercial scale. Nitrogen gas is obtained from the fractional distillation of air, and hydrogen is produced from water (or methane). The main reaction in the Haber process is:

$$N_2 + 3H_2 \rightleftharpoons 2NH_3$$

An iron catalyst is used. The reaction is carried out at a pressure of 150–300 atmospheres. A temperature of about 400°C is used. Under these conditions about 25–50% of nitrogen and hydrogen are converted to ammonia, depending on the actual conditions used.

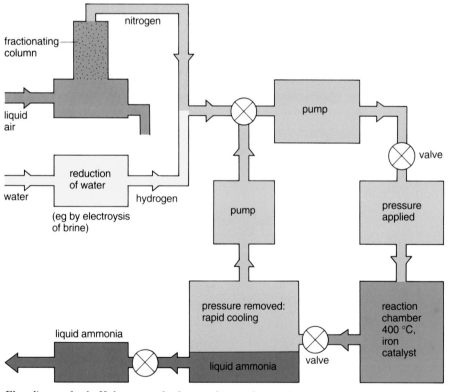

Flow diagram for the Haber process for the manufacture of ammonia

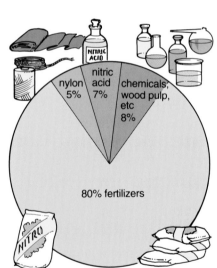

Uses of ammonia

## Activities

1 Find out what chemicals are contained in fertilizers.

2 Find out what an NPK fertilizer is.

3 Fertilizers can be easily washed into rivers and streams. What effect does this have on our drinking water and on the life forms in the rivers and streams?

## Questions

1 Draw a flow diagram to show the Haber process.

2 How is the manufacture of ammonia speeded up?

3 More ammonia could be made by increasing the pressure to 400 atmospheres. Why do you think this pressure is not used in the Haber process?

# Rate of reaction: the Contact process

The starting material for the production of sulphuric acid is sulphur. There are two main sources of sulphur. Some of it is mined from underground deposits in the USA. It is also obtained from fossil fuels before they are burnt. This reduces the pollution when these fuels are burned.

The first stage in the Contact process is the manufacture of sulphur dioxide.

$$S + O_2 \rightarrow SO_2$$

The sulphur dioxide is then filtered and cooled before being reacted with more oxygen to make sulphur trioxide.

$$2SO_2 + O_2 \rightleftharpoons 2SO_3$$

This is an equilibrium reaction. A catalyst of vanadium(V) oxide converts the sulphur dioxide to sulphur trioxide. The catalyst is used in the form of pellets to increase its surface area, hence the name the Contact process. A temperature of 450°C is used. The sulphur trioxide is then absorbed in 98% sulphuric acid. Water cannot be used to absorb sulphur trioxide as a sulphuric acid mist would be formed. This cannot be condensed and would cause pollution. Water is added to the acid mixture to produce concentrated sulphuric acid.

## Uses of sulphuric acid

130 million tonnes of sulphuric acid are produced in the world each year. About 32% is used in the manufacture of fertilizers. Other uses include the manufacture of paints, soaps, detergents, fibres, and plastics.

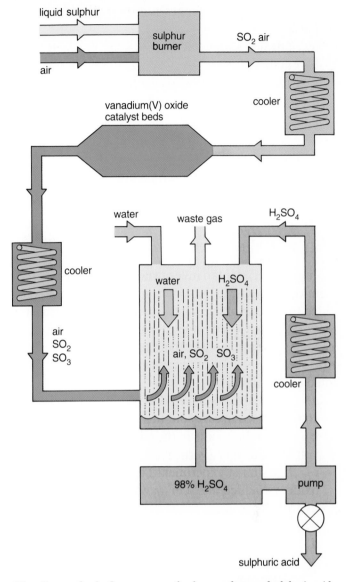

*Flow diagram for the Contact process for the manufacture of sulphuric acid*

## Questions

**1** All the reactions in the Contact process give off heat. How can this help to keep the costs of manufacture to a minimum?

**2** Write equations for the three main reactions in the Contact process.

**3** Most of the sulphur used in this process is imported from the USA by ship. It is very costly to transport the sulphur across land. What is the best site for a sulphuric acid plant and why?

**4** List the uses of sulphuric acid.

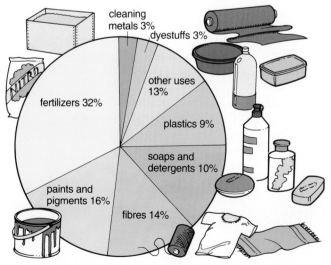

*Uses of sulphuric acid*

**1** List the following changes as chemical or non-chemical:
- **a)** burning a firework
- **b)** making ice
- **c)** adding sugar to a cup of coffee
- **d)** adding magnesium to dilute sulphuric acid
- **e)** melting iron.

**2** Classify the following reactions as decomposition, oxidation, or reduction:
- **a)** calcium carbonate → calcium oxide + carbon dioxide
- **b)** iron + oxygen → iron oxide
- **c)** silver chloride → silver + chlorine
- **d)** lead oxide + hydrogen → lead + water

**3** In an experiment to investigate the rate of a chemical reaction, 1.0 g of manganese(IV) oxide was added to 100 cm$^3$ of hydrogen peroxide. The hydrogen peroxide decomposed into water and oxygen. The reaction was carried out at room temperature and pressure. The volume of oxygen gas given off was noted every minute.
- **a)** Draw a fully labelled diagram of apparatus that could be used to carry out this experiment.
- **b)** Using the results in the table, plot a graph of volume of oxygen (vertical axis) against time.
- **c)** In a similar experiment 1 g of manganese(IV) oxide was added to 25 cm$^3$ of water and 75 cm$^3$ of hydrogen peroxide. What effect do you think this will have on the rate of reaction?
- **d)** Manganese(IV) oxide is a catalyst that speeds up the rate of decomposition of hydrogen peroxide. If you were given 1 g of copper(II) oxide how could you compare its effectiveness as a catalyst with that of manganese(IV) oxide?

**4** Iodine monochloride, ICl, reacts easily with chlorine gas, $Cl_2$. The solid iodine trichloride, $ICl_3$, is formed. However, the iodine trichloride, $ICl_3$, is not very stable and decomposes at room temperature back into chlorine and iodine monochloride:

$$ICl(l) \quad + \quad Cl_2(g) \quad \rightleftharpoons \quad ICl_3(s)$$

- **a)** What does the symbol ⇌ mean?
- **b)** What effect would adding more chlorine have on the reaction?
- **c)** How could you increase the amount of $ICl_3$ formed?
- **d)** What do the symbols (l), (g), and (s) mean?

**5** Hydrogen gas was passed over 8.0 g of heated iron oxide in the laboratory. The reaction was stopped after 30 minutes. The mass of iron obtained was weighed and found to be 5.6 g.
- **a)** Draw a fully labelled diagram of apparatus that could be used to carry out this experiment.
- **b)** What is reduction?
- **c)** What is the reducing agent in this reaction?
- **d)** Write a word equation for the reaction.
- **e)** Explain why the mass of the iron oxide is greater than the mass of the iron left after the experiment.
- **f)** The formula for iron oxide is $Fe_2O_3$. Write a full, balanced chemical equation for the reaction.
- **g)** Another student carried out the same reaction using the same amount of iron oxide. However, the reaction was stopped after 20 minutes. This time, the mass of 'iron' at the end was found to be 6.1 g. Give a reason why this might be.

| time in minutes | volume in cm$^3$ |
|:---:|:---:|
| 0 | 0 |
| 1 | 40 |
| 2 | 66 |
| 3 | 88 |
| 4 | 104 |
| 5 | 116 |
| 6 | 118 |
| 7 | 120 |
| 8 | 120 |

*What are acids?*
*Where can we find acids?*
*What are the effects of acids?*
*How can we neutralize acids?*
*How useful are acids?*

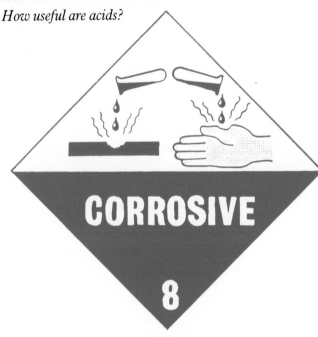

*This warning label is found on all bottles of acid.*

*All acids must be handled with care. They can cause damage to skin and clothing. Eyes should be protected, when using acids.*

Milk that has turned sour contains an acid called lactic acid. Lemon juice and vinegar both contain acid and taste 'sharp' or 'sour'. There are a great many **acids** around us in everyday life. Some 'natural' acids are given in the table below.

| name of acid | where it is found |
|---|---|
| hydrochloric | in the stomach |
| ethanoic | vinegar |
| methanoic | ants and stinging nettles |
| citric | lemon juice |
| lactic | sour milk |
| oxalic | rhubarb |
| ascorbic | fruits and vegetables |
| tartaric | grapes |
| tannic | tea |

Acids that are used in the laboratory are much more corrosive than acids found naturally. If laboratory acids are spilt on clothing or skin they can cause a great deal of damage and must be washed off immediately with plenty of water.

## Acids in the body

The hydrochloric acid found in the stomach helps to break down food. Carbohydrates and proteins are broken down into smaller, more digestible compounds such as glucose and amino acids. Too much hydrochloric acid in the stomach can cause indigestion (see page 90).

The chemical balance of the blood is essential for a healthy life. Too much acid in the blood would be fatal. Special chemicals in the blood prevent the balance being affected by too much acid (see page 81).

*What natural acids do these foods contain?*

*Look carefully at labels like these. What acids are contained in these foods and drinks?*

*Care must be taken with leaking batteries. They contain sulphuric acid. How could the spilt acid be cleared up safely?*

## Acids in food and drink

Many fruits contain acids. This gives them their slightly 'sour' or 'sharp' taste. Many foods like sauces and pickles contain ethanoic acid (vinegar). Vinegar preserves fruits and vegetables. If wine is exposed to the air for too long, the alcohol in it turns into vinegar.

Fizzy drinks are made by adding carbon dioxide gas to the drink under pressure. When carbon dioxide dissolves in water, a very weak acid, carbonic acid, is formed.

## Other uses of acids

The acids you see in the laboratory have a great many uses. Sulphuric acid is used in car batteries and as a raw material for making many other chemicals (see page 83). About 2.5 million tonnes of sulphuric acid are manufactured in the UK each year. Nitric acid is another commonly used acid. At least three-quarters of the 770 000 tonnes of nitric acid manufactured in the UK each year is used to make fertilizers. Nitric acid is also used to make explosives.

## Acid rain

All rainwater contains a small amount of acid. Rain dissolves carbon dioxide from the air, making carbonic acid. However, other gases produced by industries such as coal-fired power stations cause rain to be much more acidic. These gases are sulphur dioxide and nitrogen dioxide. When they dissolve in water, they form sulphurous and nitrous acids. Burning fossil fuels such as coal and oil give off these gases creating acid rain. The damage done by acid rain is extensive. In many areas of Scandinavia, fish in the lakes are dying. Whole forests in Germany and Scandinavia are severely affected. Buildings are crumbling and metal constructions are rusting much faster because of acid rain.

*Effects of acid rain*

## Activities

1 Find out as much as you can about acid rain. Ask environmental pressure groups and local power stations. Present your findings as a report.

2 Carry out a survey in your own home, and list all the acids and their uses you can find.

## Measuring the strengths of acids

Some acids are weak enough for us to eat, for example, vinegar. However, other acids such as sulphuric acid can be very strong. The strength of an acid is measured by its **pH**. Every acid contains hydrogen ions, $H^+$. The stronger the acid, the more hydrogen ions there are. pH is a symbol meaning **strength of acid** and comes from the German word 'potenz'. **The lower the pH number, the stronger the acid.** An acid with a pH of 1 is much stronger than an acid with a pH of 4. A substance which has a pH of 7 is **neutral**. Pure water has a pH of 7. A chemical with a pH greater than 7 is called an **alkali**. The higher the pH, the more alkaline the chemical is. An alkali with a pH of 14 is much stronger than an alkali with a pH of 9.

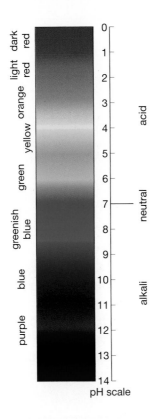

*Universal indicator is a different colour in solutions of different pH.*

The **strength** of an acid must not be confused with its **concentration**. Concentration depends on the amount of water present. Strength refers to the number of hydrogen ions. It is possible to have a dilute solution of a strong acid. For example, dilute nitric acid is a dilute solution of a strong acid. It has a pH of about 2, but is not very concentrated.

## Indicators

An **indicator** is a dye that changes colour when it is put into an acid or an alkali. There are a number of different indicators. Many are made from plant extracts. **Litmus** is an indicator made from lichen. In neutral water it has a mauve colour. This turns red when acid is added to it. When it is put into an alkali, it turns blue. Indicators can be used in solution or as paper soaked in the solution and then dried.

| indicator | colour in acid | colour in alkali |
|---|---|---|
| litmus | red | blue |
| phenolphthalein | colourless | pink |
| methyl orange | orange | yellow |
| bromothymol blue | yellow | blue |

*Some indicators and their colours*

**Universal indicator** is a mixture of several indicators. It gives a different colour at each pH number.

### Activities

**1**   Using either red cabbage or raw beetroot, you can make your own indicator.

–   Cut up the cabbage or beetroot into very small pieces.

–   Boil it in a little water for five minutes.

–   Leave to cool.

–   Strain and collect the juice.

–   Use the juice to test an acid such as lemon juice.

–   Test some baking powder (an alkali) with your indicator. What colour was the indicator in water, acid, and alkali?

–   Repeat the activity using other plant material or coloured flower petals.

# Properties and reactions of acids

## Properties of acids

- Acids are soluble in water.
- Acids turn blue litmus red.
- Acids contain hydrogen and produce $H^+$ ions in solution.
- Acids conduct electricity (they are **electrolytes**).
- Acids have a sour taste.
- Acids have a pH of less than 7.

| name of acid | formula |
|---|---|
| hydrochloric | HCl |
| nitric | $HNO_3$ |
| sulphuric | $H_2SO_4$ |
| phosphoric | $H_3PO_4$ |
| ethanoic (acetic) | $CH_3CO_2H$ |

## Metals and acids

Many metals including magnesium and calcium react with dilute acids. However, there are some metals which do not react even with concentrated acids. Gold is an example. When metals react, they displace hydrogen from the acid. During the reaction a salt is also formed. For example, zinc reacts with dilute hydrochloric acid making zinc chloride and giving off hydrogen gas.

| **metal** | + | **acid** | → | **salt** | + | **hydrogen** |
|---|---|---|---|---|---|---|
| zinc | + | hydrochloric acid | → | zinc chloride | + | hydrogen |
| Zn | + | 2HCl | → | $ZnCl_2$ | + | $H_2$ |

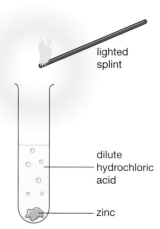

*If a lighted splint is placed near the mouth of the test tube, the hydrogen explodes with a 'squeaky pop'.*

## Carbonates and acids

All **metal carbonates** eg calcium carbonate react with dilute acids giving off carbon dioxide gas. During the reaction 'fizzing' or **effervescence** is usually seen and heard.

| calcium carbonate | + | hydrochloric acid | → | calcium chloride | + | water | + | carbon dioxide |
|---|---|---|---|---|---|---|---|---|
| $CaCO_3$ | + | 2HCl | → | $CaCl_2$ | + | $H_2O$ | + | $CO_2$ |

Carbon dioxide does not burn. Fire extinguishers are available that use the reaction of an acid with a carbonate to produce carbon dioxide foam.

The chemical test for carbon dioxide is to bubble it through **limewater** (calcium hydroxide solution).

### Activities

1  Devise experiments to test the following:

   **a)**  brown eggshells contain more carbonate than white eggshells

   **b)**  stomach powders contain carbonate

   **c)**  lemon juice is a stronger acid than vinegar.

## Carbonates and baking cakes

Some cake recipes use flour and baking powder. Baking powder is a mixture of bicarbonate of soda (sodium hydrogencarbonate) and a weak acid called cream of tartar. It is used to make cakes rise during cooking. If less raising power is needed in a recipe, then bicarbonate of soda is used on its own. When bicarbonate of soda is heated or reacted with an acid, carbon dioxide gas is given off. The carbon dioxide produced by either method produces minute bubbles, making the cake mixture rise.

*The reaction between a carbonate and an acid is useful in baking cakes.*

# Neutralization

If a metal such as magnesium reacts with a dilute acid the hydrogen in the acid is replaced by the metal. When the reaction is complete the acid is said to have been **neutralized**. Metal carbonates also neutralize acids. When an acid is neutralized a salt and water are formed. During the reaction, the pH of the acid changes. The reaction is complete and the acid neutralized when the pH of the solution reaches 7. The salt formed during the reaction depends upon which acid and which metal is used. Different acids make different salts, as shown in the table below.

| name of acid | chemical formula | name of salt |
|---|---|---|
| hydrochloric | HCl | chloride |
| nitric | $HNO_3$ | nitrate |
| sulphuric | $H_2SO_4$ | sulphate |
| phosphoric | $H_3PO_4$ | phosphate |
| ethanoic (acetic) | $CH_3CO_2H$ | ethanoate (acetate) |

A chemical that neutralizes an acid is called a **base**. Metal oxides and hydroxides both react with acids to make a salt and water.

**acid + metal oxide → salt + water**
**acid + metal hydroxide → salt + water**

For example, when copper(II) oxide reacts with dilute sulphuric acid the familiar blue salt of copper(II) sulphate is formed.

sulphuric acid + copper(II) oxide → copper(II) sulphate + water
$H_2SO_4$ + CuO → $CuSO_4$ + $H_2O$

The copper(II) sulphate crystals can be recovered by heating the solution gently to evaporate the excess water, as shown in the top diagram.

The salt formed in the reaction of sodium hydroxide with dilute hydrochloric acid is often called **table salt**. Its correct chemical name is sodium chloride, NaCl.

hydrochloric acid + sodium hydroxide → sodium chloride + water
HCl + NaOH → NaCl + $H_2O$

Ammonium hydroxide also neutralizes acids – this is an exception as it is a salt which does not contain a metal.

## Understanding neutralization

An **ion** is a charged particle. All acids contain hydrogen ions, $H^+$. For example, hydrochloric acid, HCl, contains hydrogen ions and chloride ions, $Cl^-$. There are the same number of hydrogen ions as chloride ions. To neutralize an acid, the hydrogen ions have to be replaced by metal ions. Sodium hydroxide contains sodium ions, $Na^+$, and hydroxide ions, $OH^-$. When the sodium ions replace the hydrogen ions, the salt sodium chloride is made, NaCl. The hydrogen ions combine with the hydroxide ions to make water, $H_2O$.

$$H^+ + OH^- \rightarrow H_2O$$

*The more slowly the water is evaporated away, the better the crystals of copper(II) sulphate. This is one way of carrying out the evaporation slowly.*

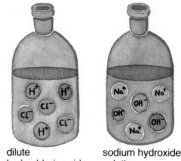

dilute hydrochloric acid

sodium hydroxide solution

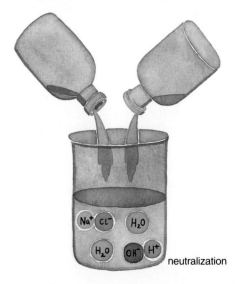

neutralization

*When dilute hydrochloric acid and sodium hydroxide solution are mixed, sodium chloride and water are produced.*

# Useful neutralization reactions

## Curing indigestion

Dilute hydrochloric acid is found in the stomach. When you suffer from indigestion, there is usually more acid in the stomach than is needed. Indigestion tablets neutralize this excess acid. They contain metal carbonates or hydroxides.

## Cleaning your teeth

During the day your teeth become coated in sugars and acids from the food you eat. Some toothpastes are slightly alkaline. They help to neutralize the effects of acids formed as a byproduct when microbes feed on sugar.

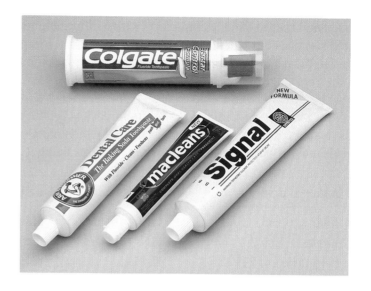

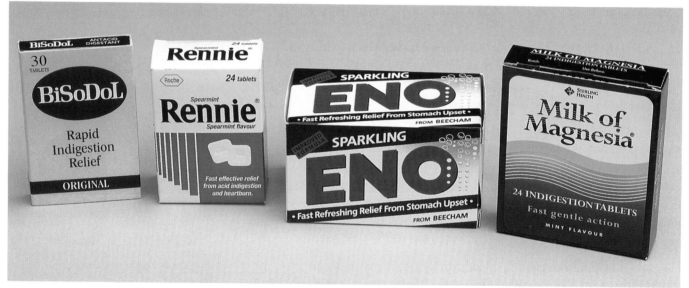

*'Antacids' contain chemicals which neutralize excess acid in the stomach. Find out which chemicals in these indigestion preparations neutralize acid.*

## Activities

1   Find three different types of indigestion tablets. Devise an experiment to test the effectiveness of each tablet. Use vinegar or lemon juice as your acid. Compare the results of your experiment with the effectiveness of using sodium hydrogencarbonate (bicarbonate of soda) as a cure for indigestion.

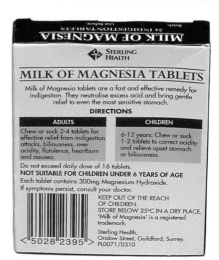

# Bases and alkalis

A **base** is a metal oxide or hydroxide. Copper oxide, magnesium oxide, and iron oxide are all bases. A base that is soluble in water is called an **alkali**, for example, sodium hydroxide. Ammonium hydroxide is also an alkali, but it does not contain a metal. Not very many bases are soluble in water. Bases and alkalis both neutralize acids. When they do so, a salt and water are formed.

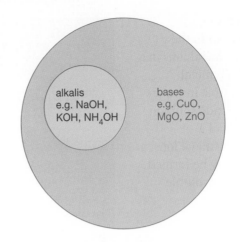

acid + base → salt + water

acid + alkali → salt + water

*Venn diagram showing how some bases are also alkalis*

## Properties and uses of alkalis

- Alkalis are soluble in water.
- Alkalis turn red litmus blue.
- Alkalis have a pH of more than 7.
- Alkalis conduct electricity when in solution (they are electrolytes).
- Alkalis are soapy to the touch.

Sodium hydroxide is used extensively in industry. It is sometimes called caustic soda. It is used to make soap and soap powders. Animal fats or vegetable oils are boiled with sodium hydroxide to form, for example, sodium stearate (soap). Because alkalis react with fats, sodium hydroxide is a useful ingredient in oven cleaners. Sodium hydroxide is also used to remove the resins from wood pulp in the manufacture of paper.

*Alkalis are used in all these products.*

Some household bleaches contain ammonium hydroxide since it is very soluble in water. Calcium hydroxide (slaked lime) is less soluble than sodium or ammonium hydroxides. When calcium hydroxide is dissolved in water it forms limewater.

| name of alkali | chemical formula |
|---|---|
| sodium hydroxide | NaOH |
| potassium hydroxide | KOH |
| ammonium hydroxide | $NH_4OH$ |
| calcium hydroxide (limewater) | $Ca(OH)_2$ |

## Questions

1  Write down the names of three alkalis.

2  Write down the names of three bases which are not alkalis.

3  List some uses of alkalis.

4  What would the pH of a strong alkali be? What colour would universal indicator be in a strong alkali?

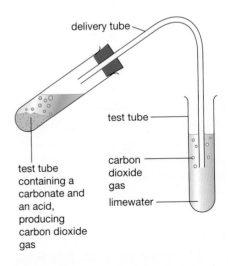

*Limewater can be used in the laboratory to test for carbon dioxide gas. When the gas is bubbled through limewater, it turns milky.*

91

# Using alkalis in the laboratory

Sodium and ammonium hydroxides can be used in the laboratory to test for metal ions in a compound. Nearly all metal hydroxides are insoluble in water. When sodium hydroxide solution is added to a solution of a compound containing metal ions, a **precipitate** (solid) may be formed. This precipitate is an insoluble metal hydroxide.

*When sodium hydroxide is added to magnesium sulphate solution, a white precipitate of magnesium hydroxide is seen.*

| metal in compound | result of adding a few drops of NaOH | result of adding excess NaOH |
|---|---|---|
| potassium | no precipitate | no precipitate |
| magnesium | white precipitate | white precipitate |
| calcium | white precipitate | white precipitate |
| zinc | white precipitate | precipitate dissolves |
| lead | white precipitate | precipitate dissolves |
| copper | blue precipitate | blue precipitate |
| iron(II) | green precipitate | green precipitate |
| iron(III) | red-brown precipitate | red-brown precipitate |

*Precipitates formed by metal ions and sodium hydroxide solution*

Alkalis can be used in the laboratory to neutralize an acid by carrying out an experiment called a **titration** (see page 94). The reaction between potassium hydroxide and hydrochloric acid can be written down in an equation.

$$\text{hydrochloric acid} + \text{potassium hydroxide} \rightarrow \text{potassium chloride} + \text{water}$$
$$HCl + KOH \rightarrow KCl + H_2O$$

Ammonium hydroxide, $NH_4OH$, does not contain any metal ions. However, it contains ammonium ions, $NH_4^+$. These ions can replace the hydrogen ions in an acid in the same way as metal ions. Salts which contain ammonium ions are used as fertilizers. Ammonium sulphate and ammonium nitrate are both fertilizers. Ammonium nitrate is made by neutralizing nitric acid with ammonium hydroxide.

## Questions

1  Name three types of chemicals that can neutralize an acid.

2  What is the difference between a base and an alkali?

3  What are the main properties of alkalis?

4  List some uses of sodium hydroxide.

5  What is always made during the neutralization of an acid?

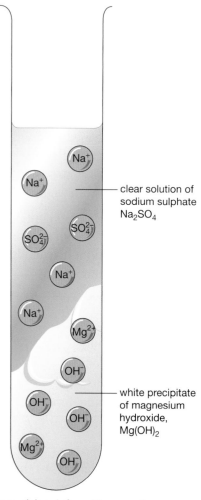

clear solution of sodium sulphate $Na_2SO_4$

white precipitate of magnesium hydroxide, $Mg(OH)_2$

*The precipitate is formed by magnesium hydroxide which is insoluble. Magnesium ions, $Mg^{2+}$, combine with hydroxide ions, $OH^-$, to form the precipitate.*

# The pH of soil

Soil contains minerals which when dissolved can make the soil acid or alkaline. Different plants prefer different conditions. This is very important to a farmer or gardener who can choose crops and control soil conditions to give the best results.

| plants suitable for acid soils (pH < 7) | plants suitable for alkaline soils (pH > 7) |
|---|---|
| azaleas<br>camellias<br>ericas (heathers)<br>lupins<br>magnolias<br>pieris<br>rhododendrons | dianthus (pinks)<br>gypsophila<br>saxifrage<br>lilac |

If a soil is too acid or alkaline, it will not produce good crops. You can measure the pH of soil using indicators. Most of the soil in Britain is slightly acidic with a pH of about 6. Soil with a pH of about 6 or 6.5 is best for growing crops, though different plants require different conditions. Wheat needs a soil pH of 6.0–7.5. When the pH of the soil becomes less than 5 little grows well, though swedes need an acidic soil of pH 4.7–5.6 for the best growth!

The use of fertilizers makes soil more acidic. If a soil becomes too acidic for good plant growth then the correct pH value can be restored by using chemicals such as lime (calcium oxide is a base). Lime has the additional benefit of improving drainage conditions. Chalk (calcium carbonate), $CaCO_3$, is often used in place of lime since it does not dissolve as readily and therefore is not washed away so easily.

## Questions

1  Why is chalk sometimes added to soil instead of lime?

2  Find out what you can add to an alkaline soil to reduce its pH.

3  What can be added to an acidic soil to improve its pH?

4  Some gardeners put the washings from their milk bottles on their garden plants. How do you think this might be useful?

*The flowers on hydrangeas are blue in acid soils and pink in alkaline soils.*

*Lime is used to increase the pH of the soil in certain areas.*

Different parts of the country have soils with different pH values. Soil in a limestone area will be alkaline. The soil on the Yorkshire Moors and in North Wales is very acidic. Wild rhododendrons which like acidic soils are growing profusely in Wales and causing problems. As time goes on, the soil will become more acidic with the fall of acid rain (see page 86).

### Finding the pH of a soil sample

1  Dry the soil samples.

2  Quarter-fill a test tube with the sample to be tested.

3  Put about $5\,cm^3$ of dilute universal indicator solution into the test tube and shake for 30 seconds.

4  Leave to settle and then note the colour and pH of the sample.

### Activities

1  Collect some soil samples from around different plants. **Remember to wear gloves when digging in the garden.** Make a note of where each sample came from, what the plant is called, and how healthy the plant looks. In the school laboratory, find out the pH of each soil sample. Write up your results in a table with the following headings.

**name of plant   health of plant   pH of soil   notes**

Write a report on your findings. Compare your results with other members of your class. Can you draw any general conclusions about the type of soil in your locality?

# Titration

When an acid and an alkali react together, a salt and water are formed. It is possible to find out exactly how much alkali is needed to neutralize an acid by carrying out a **titration**. This is an experiment using equipment that can measure the volume of a solution accurately. The reaction between hydrochloric acid and sodium hydroxide can be carried out as a titration.

hydrochloric acid + sodium hydroxide → sodium chloride + water
HCl + NaOH → NaCl + H$_2$O

A safety pipette filler is used to fill a pipette with a measured amount of alkali. The alkali is placed in a conical flask and a few drops of indicator are added. The acid is placed in a burette. Acid is then added to the alkali carefully, a small amount at a time. When the alkali has just neutralized the acid, the indicator changes colour. This is called the **neutral point** or **end-point**. The conical flask now contains a salt and water. If the salt is required, the titration is repeated without the indicator using exactly the same amounts of acid and alkali. The salt can be obtained by evaporating the water away. The table gives the results of a titration between hydrochloric acid and 25cm$^3$ of 1.0 M sodium hydroxide using universal indicator.

| volume of 1.0 M HCl added in cm$^3$ | colour of indicator |
|---|---|
| 0 | purple |
| 5 | purple |
| 10 | blue |
| 15 | blue |
| 20 | blue |
| 21 | blue |
| 22 | blue |
| 23 | blue |
| 24 | green |
| 25 | yellow |
| 26 | pink |
| 27 | pink |
| 28 | pink |
| 29 | pink |
| 30 | pink |
| (Volume of 1.0 M NaOH used = 25 cm$^3$) | |

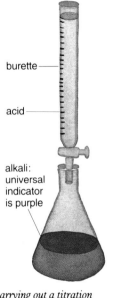

burette

acid

alkali: universal indicator is purple

pipette

dilute sodium hydroxide 25 cm$^3$

25cm³

*Apparatus for carrying out a titration*

## Questions

1  What is a titration?

2  What is meant by **neutral point** or **end-point**?

3  Draw a labelled diagram of the apparatus used in a titration.

4  What colour is universal indicator in a neutral solution?

5  Look at the table of results for the titration between hydrochloric acid and sodium hydroxide. How many cubic centimetres of acid are neutralized by 25 cm$^3$ of sodium hydroxide?

6  If the indicator litmus was used, what colour would it be at the end-point of the titration?

*Titrations are carried out in analyical laboratories to find the concentrations of solutions.*

# Solubility of salts

A salt is made when an acid is neutralized. The name of the salt made depends on the acid and the compound used to neutralize it. Nearly all salts are soluble in water. Sodium chloride, NaCl, is the most common salt. It is often just called salt. It is used to add taste to our food, and in its raw form on icy roads. However, 'salt' is a word that describes a group of chemicals all having the same properties.

- Salts have high melting points.

- Salts have high boiling points.

- Salts are often soluble in water.

- Salts can conduct electricity when dissolved in water or in the liquid state (they form electrolytes).

Some salts contain water in their crystals. These are **hydrated** salts. The water in their crystals is called **water of crystallization**. For example, blue copper(II) sulphate crystals have the formula $CuSO_4.5H_2O$. If this hydrated salt is heated, the water of crystallization is lost and white **anhydrous** copper(II) sulphate is left.

If you want to make a salt in the laboratory, it is important to know whether it is **soluble** in water or not. A salt is described as soluble if more than 1 g of the salt dissolves in 100 g of water.

- All sodium, potassium and ammonium salts are soluble.

- All nitrates are soluble.

- All chlorides are soluble except silver and lead chlorides.

- All sulphates are soluble except silver, lead, barium, and calcium sulphates.

- All carbonates, sulphides, and sulphites are insoluble except those of sodium, potassium, and ammonium.

## Preparing an insoluble salt

Insoluble salts can be prepared by precipitation. For example, if you want to make some silver chloride salt, you add a solution containing silver ions to one containing chloride ions. When these two solutions are added together, a precipitate is formed. This can be filtered, washed, and left to dry. Suitable solutions for making silver chloride would be silver nitrate and sodium chloride. Both of these salts are soluble in water.

## Questions

1  How much of a salt must dissolve in 100 g of water if the salt is soluble?

2  What is meant by **water of crystallization**?

3  Make a list of five soluble salts and five insoluble salts.

4  Describe how you could prepare a pure, dry sample of the salt lead sulphate from lead nitrate solution and sodium sulphate solution.

*Salting a road in winter.*

*Sodium chloride forms cubic crystals.*

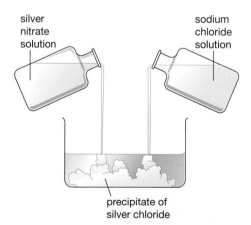

*When a solution containing silver ions, $Ag^+$, is added to a solution containing chloride ions, $Cl^-$, a precipitate of silver chloride is produced.*

95

# Solubility and making crystals

## Solubility

When a solid dissolves in a liquid, a solution is formed. The maximum amount of solid that will dissolve depends on the amount of liquid used and the temperature of the liquid. For example, you can dissolve 36 g of sodium chloride (salt) in 100 g of water at 20 °C. If you add any more salt, it will just sink to the bottom as a solid. We say the solution is **saturated**. If you want to dissolve the extra salt, you can either add more water or heat the solution.

The graph opposite shows how much copper(II) sulphate will dissolve in 100 g of water at different temperatures. This is called a **solubility curve**.

Notice that at 55 °C, a saturated solution containing 100 g of water holds 37 g of copper(II) sulphate. If this is cooled to 15 °C, it can only hold 19 g of copper(II) sulphate. The rest (18 g) has to come out of the solution. As it does so, it forms crystals.

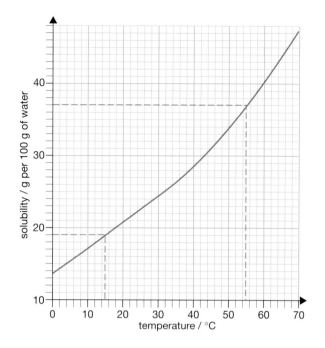

*The solubility curve for copper(II) sulphate.*

## Activities

1 **Making a saturated solution of copper(II) sulphate**
   a) Measure 50 cm³ of pure water into a small beaker.
   b) Add two heaped spatulas of hydrated copper(II) sulphate powder.
   c) Stir until the powder has been dissolved.
   d) Keep adding the copper sulphate until no more will dissolve.
   e) Warm the solution.
   f) Add some more copper(II) sulphate and stir. When no more will dissolve you have a saturated solution.
   g) Leave the saturated solution to cool completely before starting to grow your crystal.

2 **Growing a crystal**
   a) Choose a small pure crystal of copper(II) sulphate and glue it to a piece of thread. (This is called a seed crystal.)
   b) Suspend the seed crystal in a saturated solution as shown in the diagram.
   c) Cover the beaker to avoid quick evaporation.
   d) After a few days you will notice that your crystal has started to grow.

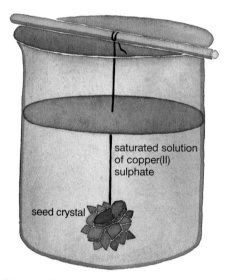

*Crystals of copper(II) sulphate can be grown to quite large sizes using this method.*

## Questions

1 Describe how you would carry out an experiment to plot a solubility curve for the soluble salt, copper nitrate. What apparatus would you need? What readings would you take?

2 Using the solubility curve above, find the mass of copper(II) sulphate that can dissolve in:
   a) 100 g of water at 30 °C   b) 200 g of water at 50 °C.

# Making soluble salts

There are four different ways of making a soluble salt.

| acid | + | metal | → | salt | + | hydrogen |
|------|---|-------|---|------|---|----------|
| acid | + | metal oxide | → | salt | + | water |
| acid | + | alkali | → | salt | + | water |
| acid | + | carbonate | → | salt | + | water | + carbon dioxide |

The method used depends on the salt you want to make. The method using the reaction between an acid and an alkali is described on page 89.

## Acid + metal

Not all metals react with dilute acids. This method cannot be used to make copper compounds, for example, since copper does not react with dilute acids. Lead reacts too slowly. Other metals, such as sodium and potassium, are too reactive to add to acid safely in the laboratory.

Zinc sulphate can be made using this method.

| sulphuric acid | + | zinc | → | zinc sulphate | + | hydrogen |
|----------------|---|------|---|---------------|---|----------|
| $H_2SO_4$ | + | $Zn$ | → | $ZnSO_4$ | + | $H_2$ |

Small amounts of zinc are added to the acid until no more reacts. When all the acid has been neutralized, there will be no more hydrogen gas given off. It is sometimes necessary to warm the flask gently to make sure that the reaction is complete. The excess zinc is filtered off. The remaining solution is crystallized to leave the salt.

## Acid + metal oxide

This reaction is carried out in a similar way to the reaction with acid + metal. However, no hydrogen gas is given off during this reaction. To make sure that all the acid has been neutralized, the reaction can be tested with blue litmus paper. If the reaction is over, the litmus paper will remain blue. If it turns red, then either more metal oxide is needed or the reaction needs to be warmed slightly. The excess metal oxide is filtered off. The solution is evaporated to leave the salt.

## Acid + metal carbonate

When a carbonate reacts with an acid, carbon dioxide gas is given off. All the acid will be neutralized if you add carbonate until no more gas is given off. The excess carbonate is filtered off. The solution is evaporated.

### Questions

**1** What are the four ways in which a soluble salt can be made in the laboratory?

**2** Draw fully labelled diagrams to describe how to make copper(II) sulphate using copper(II) carbonate and sulphuric acid.

**3** Which method could you use to prepare the following salts:
  **a)** magnesium chloride
  **b)** copper(II) chloride
  **c)** sodium sulphate
  **d)** calcium nitrate?

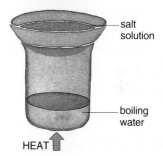

*Making zinc sulphate from zinc and sulphuric acid*

*Geologists test rocks for carbonates by adding a few drops of acid.*

Salt is found underground as rock salt. In the UK it is mined in Cheshire. This rock salt is put on icy roads in the winter. The salt lowers the freezing point of water to below 0 °C. Salt water speeds up rusting (see page 48), so it is very important to wash cars carefully and frequently in the winter.

The correct amount of salt is very important in our diets. Too little salt can cause circulation problems. When we perspire, we lose a lot of salt through the pores of our skin. In very hot conditions people take salt tablets. However, too much salt is bad for you. It can cause high blood pressure and heart disease. Before the days of refrigeration, salt was used to preserve food. Pork was covered in salt and left in a cool building – it could be eaten months later.

The sea contains about 25 g of sodium chloride per litre of sea water. Sea water also contains many other salts, as shown in the table below.

| salt found | amount in g per 100 g sea water |
|---|---|
| sodium chloride | 2.6 |
| magnesium chloride | 0.3 |
| magnesium sulphate | 0.2 |
| calcium sulphate | 0.1 |
| potassium chloride | 0.1 |
| magnesium bromide | 0.01 |
| magnesium iodide | 0.0003 |

Salt is the main raw material for making chlorine and sodium hydroxide. A concentrated salt solution, called **brine**, is electrolysed.

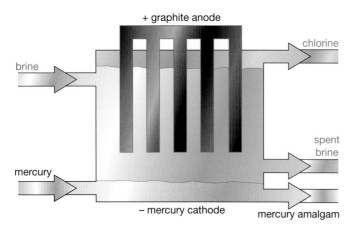

*Flowing mercury cathode cell*

## Reactions at the electrodes

When brine is electrolysed the reactions at the anode and cathode are:

*anode* ( + )

$$2Cl^- - 2e^- \rightarrow Cl_2$$
(Two chloride ions give up their electrons to form one chlorine molecule $Cl_2$.)

*cathode* ( − )

$$Na^+ + e^- \rightarrow Na$$
(Each sodium ion gains an electron to become a sodium atom, Na.)

## Salts as fertilizers

Ammonium nitrate is a useful fertilizer. It is a salt. It contains nitrogen which is an element essential for plant growth. A good fertilizer contains the elements needed to promote healthy growth in plants. It must also be cheap to produce and soluble in water.

*Ammonium nitrate is used as a fertilizer.*

In industry, ammonium nitrate is made by reacting ammonia with nitric acid. For this reason, the manufacture of ammonia and nitric acid are often carried out close to each other to reduce costs. Ammonia gas can be used directly as a fertilizer, but needs to be compressed to a liquid before it is injected into the Earth. This method is very popular in the USA.

Some other salts that are used as fertilizers include:

- calcium nitrate, $Ca(NO_3)_2$
- sodium nitrate, $NaNO_3$
- ammonium phosphate, $(NH_4)_3 PO_4$
- ammonium sulphate, $(NH_4)_2 SO_4$
- potassium sulphate, $K_2SO_4$.

1   Copy and complete the following table:

| name of chemical | pH | colour of universal indicator |
|---|---|---|
|  | 1 |  |
| pure water |  |  |
|  | 14 |  |
|  |  | blue |

2   Answer the following questions in full sentences:
a)  What indicator turns red in lemon juice and blue in sodium carbonate solution?
b)  The 'fur' inside kettles is mostly calcium hydrogencarbonate. What household chemical could be used to 'defur' a kettle?
c)  A gardener wishes to grow some turnips. They grow best in soil with a pH of 6. The soil in the garden is at a pH of 5.5. What could the gardener do to the soil to improve the chances of a good crop of turnips?

3   The labels have gone missing from four bottles. The bottles are known to contain the following colourless solutions:

• phenolphthalein
• hydrochloric acid
• sodium hydroxide
• sodium carbonate.

Using only test tubes and four pieces of magnesium, design an experiment to determine which bottle is which. Describe the results you would expect.

4   a)  List three differences between a mixture and a compound.
b)  Give two examples of a mixture and two examples of a compound.
c)  Describe how you could separate water from a solution of black ink in the laboratory.

5   What is the name of the salt that is made when the following chemicals react?
a)  phosphoric acid + potassium carbonate
b)  sulphuric acid + magnesium oxide
c)  hydrochloric acid + ammonium hydroxide
d)  nitric acid + zinc
e)  hydrochloric acid + silver nitrate.

6   Give brief details of how the following salts could be prepared in the laboratory:
a)  potassium chloride
b)  copper(II) nitrate
c)  lead chloride
d)  magnesium sulphate.

7   a)  Describe what you would see if a piece of zinc metal was placed in some dilute hydrochloric acid.
b)  How would you identify the gas that was given off during the reaction?
c)  Write an equation for the reaction.

8   What is the difference between a strong acid and a concentrated acid? What type of experiments could you carry out to illustrate your answer? Use ethanoic (acetic) acid (vinegar) and hydrochloric acid to help you answer this question.

9   Sodium chloride is 'common or table salt'.
a)  What chemicals can be obtained from the electrolysis of sodium chloride?
b)  List the uses of common salt and the chemicals made from it.
c)  What effects does sodium chloride have on our health?

*Are all the rocks that make up the Earth the same?*
*How were rocks formed?*
*What is the rock cycle?*

Today, the surface of our planet, Earth, is made up of three different types of rock: **igneous**, **sedimentary**, and **metamorphic**. These were formed in different ways.

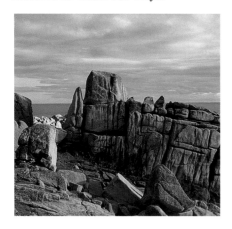

**Igneous rocks**: *form when molten (liquid) rock from under the Earth comes to the surface and solidifies. Volcanoes are the most obvious evidence of the formation of igneous rocks! The picture shows* **granite**.

**Sedimentary rocks**: *igneous rocks are broken down by physical and chemical processes on the Earth's surface. The resulting pieces can be carried away by rivers and deposited in layers under the sea. High pressures produce new, hard, sedimentary rocks. The picture shows* **sandstone**.

**Metamorphic rocks**: *sedimentary rocks beneath the Earth's surface are placed under great pressure. They are also heated by hot, molten rock. This can change them into new, metamorphic rocks. The picture shows* **slate**.

Millions of years ago, when the Earth was first formed, the surface must have consisted entirely of igneous rocks. As the years rolled slowly by, the igneous rocks gradually changed into sedimentary rocks. Slowly these sedimentary rocks were pushed under the Earth's surface, where they changed into metamorphic rocks.

Over millions of years, the rock types change from one to the other over and over again. This is called the **rock cycle**.

### Questions

1   Suggest why were there no sedimentary rocks when the Earth first formed.

2   'Metamorphic' means 'changed form'.
    **a)** Write down two words beginning with 'meta' which are related to change. Give their meanings.
    **b)** Write down two words containing 'morph' meaning shape or form. Give their meanings.

3   Use a reference book or other source of information to find out how old the Earth is.

*Far beneath the oceans, where the Earth's crust is thinnest, new igneous rocks and minerals come to the surface. Here copper and iron sulphides pour out in a 'black smoker'.*

# The rock cycle: igneous rocks

Rocks are being made all around us now. This may be hard to believe since rocks always seem to be static things that never change. However, if we lived for ten thousand years we would be able to observe the ways in which one rock is gradually produced from another. This is part of **the rock cycle**.

**Igneous rocks** form the starting point in the rock cycle. Igneous rocks are sometimes called volcanic rocks because they are produced by the solidification on the Earth's surface of molten rock from volcanoes.

The molten rock or **magma** comes from the mantle of the Earth. Most volcanic rocks are crystalline. The size of the crystals depends upon how long the magma takes to cool down. Slow cooling gives big crystals and rapid cooling gives small crystals. All the material from which other rocks have been made originally came from igneous rocks.

The following diagram tells you more about volcanoes and igneous rocks.

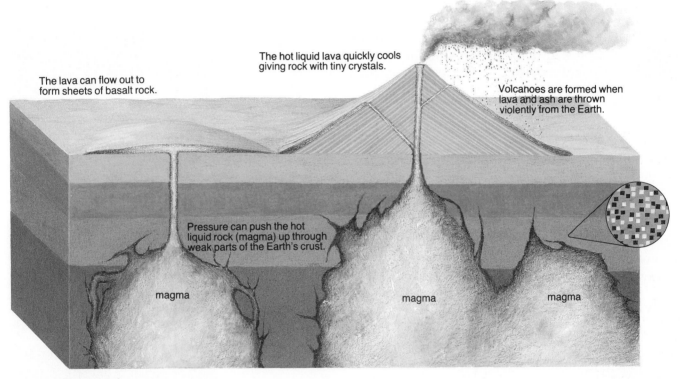

The hot liquid lava quickly cools giving rock with tiny crystals.

The lava can flow out to form sheets of basalt rock.

Volcanoes are formed when lava and ash are thrown violently from the Earth.

Pressure can push the hot liquid rock (magma) up through weak parts of the Earth's crust.

magma

magma

magma

*Formation of igneous rocks*

## Questions

**1** *Ignis* is the latin word for 'fire'. Why do you think volcanic rocks are called 'igneous'?

**2** What is magma? Where is it formed?

**3** Why are most igneous rocks crystalline?

**4** Suggest why granite contains larger crystals than basalt.

**5** Why is diamond so hard?

**6** Why does pumice float?

**Diamond** *(carbon), the hardest natural substance, is formed in volcanic rock where temperature and pressure are very high.*

*Bubbles of gas are often released from molten lava making it frothy. When this solidifies a rock called* **pumice** *is formed – it floats.*

# The rock cycle: sedimentary rocks (1)

Once igneous rocks are exposed to the atmosphere on the surface of the Earth, they start to be broken down. The silicate minerals of the igneous rocks are attacked by chemical and physical processes that lead to their destruction. This is known as **weathering**. The products of the weathering action accumulate to form **sedimentary rocks**. Sandstone, clay, limestone and chalk are sedimentary rocks.

There are two main types of weathering: physical and chemical.

## Physical weathering

Rocks can be worn away or **eroded** by the action of wind but perhaps the best example of physical weathering is frost shattering. Water seeps into cracks in the rocks and then freezes. As it turns to ice it expands and forces the rock to split. Large boulders fall and shatter to form **scree** at the foot of mountain slopes. You can see the effect of frost action on road surfaces after a severe winter.

*Scree*

## Chemical weathering

Scree fragments and exposed rock faces are open to attack by rainwater. Rainwater absorbs carbon dioxide from the air, making it slightly acidic. Chemical reactions take place between the water and the rock minerals, causing them to crumble and possibly be dissolved and carried away.

Some minerals such as quartz are not affected by chemical weathering, whereas others like feldspar are broken down to clay minerals. In Cornwall the minerals in the granite have been broken down to form china clay – the basis of the North Staffordshire pottery industry.

## Example: the weathering of limestone

Limestone is mainly made up of calcium carbonate. It reacts with mildly acidic rainwater. When rainwater runs over limestone it reacts with the rock, causing it to erode. This **weathering** of limestone causes the formation of caves in limestone areas.

$$CaCO_3 + H_2O + CO_2 \rightarrow Ca(HCO_3)_2$$

calcium       water       carbon       calcium hydrogencarbonate
carbonate                dioxide       solution

Sometimes the reaction is reversible. A drop of water might hang from the roof of a cave, having already reacted with the limestone. The water evaporates into the surrounding air, leaving particles of solid calcium carbonate behind. Over thousands of years, enough calcium carbonate is deposited to form a **stalactite**. Water dripping on the floor causes **stalagmites** to form.

*Stalactites and stalagmites are deposits of calcium carbonate. Stalactites grow down from the ceiling. Stalagmites grow up from the floor.*

## Questions

1  What is weathering?

2  What does the word 'eroded' mean?

3  Explain why a very cold winter damages road surfaces.

4  Describe how stalactites are formed.

5  What is the difference between a stalactite and a stalagmite?

# The rock cycle: sedimentary rocks (2)

## Transporting the weathered material

The diagram shows how rock particles created by weathering are carried to the sea.

*1 Weathering breaks down the rocks into fragments. These are carried by wind or washed by rain into streams and rivers.*

*2 Rivers carry the rock fragments into the sea (or into a lake). The surface of the rocks become smoothed off to form pebbles. The faster a river flows, the bigger the pebbles it can carry.*

*3 When it reaches the sea, the river slows down. Pebbles and smaller particles such as sand and gravel are deposited on the sea bed, forming layers of sediment.*

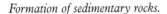

*Formation of sedimentary rocks.*

Over millions of years sediment will pile up, forcing water out of the lower layers and compacting them together, eventually forming rock. The size and origin of the sediment particles will determine the type of sedimentary rock that is produced. Sandstone, for example, is formed from compacted sand grains. Limestone contains a large proportion of organic material such as calcium carbonate from the shells and skeletons of marine creatures.

*Pebbles, sand and very small particles of rock (silt) are deposited at river estuaries like this. Sometimes so much material is deposited that the river has to be dredged to clear a channel for boats.*

*This is limestone, a sedimentary rock formed in the sea. Can you see the fossils in this rock? How did they form?*

## Questions

1 How do rock fragments from mountains get into the sea?

2 David finds that a river bed is covered with smooth, round pebbles. How did these form?

3 What is the relationship between the speed of a river and the size of stones it can carry?

4 Suggest why river sand has larger grains than sand found on the seashore.

5 How is sedimentary rock made?

# The rock cycle: metamorphic rocks

Metamorphism means 'change of form'. Many sedimentary and igneous rocks have been subjected to mechanical forces, squeezing and pushing, and to different conditions of temperature and pressure since they were formed. These processes produce a new group of rocks called **metamorphic rocks**.

For example, rock can be changed when very hot magma is pushed up into it. Where the magma pushes into other rocks, it is called an **intrusion**. The size of the intrusion is important. Small intrusions will not heat up the surrounding rock as much as large ones. The diagram shows how the metamorphic rocks marble and quartzite are made as a result of a magma intrusion into bands of sedimentary limestone and sandstone. Rather like a cake being baked, the end product is very different to the original mixture.

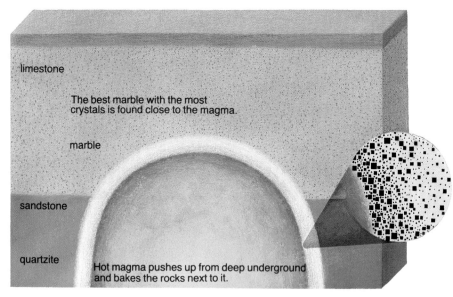

limestone

The best marble with the most crystals is found close to the magma.

marble

sandstone

quartzite

Hot magma pushes up from deep underground and bakes the rocks next to it.

*Making metamorphic rocks*

Metamorphic rocks are extemely hard (like burnt cakes!) and usually have a spotty appearance due to the formation of new minerals inside them. The type of rock formed depends upon the area of contact between the magma intrusion and the surrounding rock. The best marble is formed immediately next to the magma.

**Regional metamorphism** affects very large masses of rock and is usually associated with mountain building. Most of the continents of the Earth are regionally metamorphosed rocks. Huge movements of the Earth subjected rocks to great pressure and high temperatures. This formed new rocks.

Slate is a dull grey rock formed when sedimentary mudstone was compressed deep underground. Mudstone grains grew into flaky crystals which were arranged in parallel layers. This is why slate splits easily into flat sheets. These have been used for many years in the building industry as roofing material. Today they are expensive to produce and have mostly been replaced by clay or cement tiles.

*Splitting slate*

## Questions

1  What is metamorphic rock?

2  Explain how marble is made.

3  Why are some statues made from marble and not limestone?

4  Explain why very old marble statues, like those in Greece, are not quite like they were when they were made.
(*Hint*: remember that rain water is slightly acid.)

5  How was slate made?

*Marble statues, badly affected by air pollution*

# And so the rock cycle is complete

When you look at a mountain or a large cliff face it is easy to think that rocks are permanent and will never change. However, it is important to realize that rocks play a temporary part in the evolution of our planet. Igneous rocks are weathered and eroded. The debris is transported then dumped to eventually become sedimentary rock. This may be buried deeply and changed by heat and pressure (metamorphism) and then be lifted to form a mountain range only to be eroded again! The rock cycle goes on and on . . .

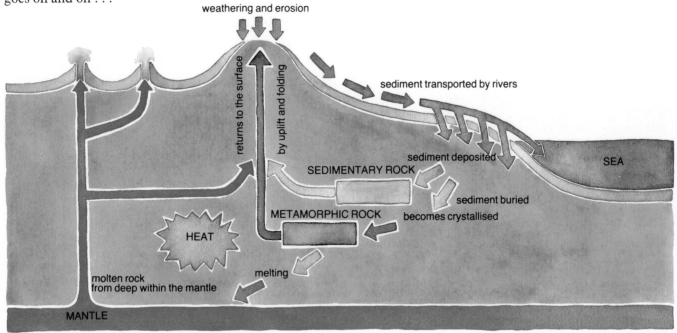

*The rock cycle*

## 'The present is the key to the past'

In the late eighteenth century James Hutton put forward one of the most important ideas in earth science. It was called **uniformitarianism**.

Hutton believed that we can understand the geological history of the Earth surface by studying the processes that we can see happening today – the rock cycle!

## Questions

1 Explain why the rock cycle is called a **cycle**.

2 In theory, material from the mantle could reach the surface and then be reburied until it became molten again.
   **a)** Describe briefly how this could happen.
   **b)** Roughly how long do you think the cycle would take?

3 Why is water important in the rock cycle?

4 'All mountains we see today were formed at the beginning of the Earth and will never change.'
Do you agree with this statement? Explain your answer.

**1** The diagram shows the rock cycle.

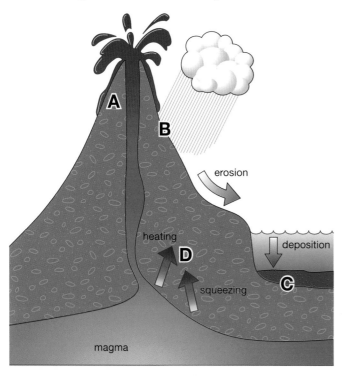

**a)** What **type** of rock would you find at A? Name one example.

**b)** What process is taking place at B?

**c)** What **type** of rock would you find at C? Name one example.

**d)** What **type** of rock would you find at D? Name one example.

**e)** What is magma?

**f)** Why is water important in the rock cycle?

**g)** "All mountains that we see today were formed at the beginning of the Earth and will never change."

Do you agree with this statement?
Explain your answer.

**2** One of the following sentences describes 'weathering'. Write down the sentence and then write the others **in correct order** after it.

- Rock particles are transported by wind or water.

- Rock is worn away by wind and water.

- Rock particles build up on top of one another in layers.

- Rock particles are deposited at the mouths of rivers.

- Rock particles are squashed together to form rock.

**3** Copy the table below. Complete it by classifying each rock as either igneous, sedimentary, or metamorphic. Give one use for each type of rock.

| rock | type | use |
|------|------|-----|
| sandstone | | |
| granite | | |
| marble | | |
| limestone | | |
| slate | | |
| pumice | | |

**4** The graph shows the range of size of rock particles that can be i) picked up and ii) deposited by different water current speeds.

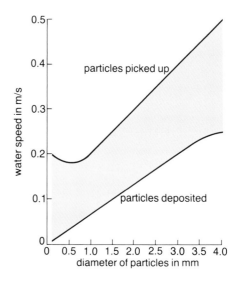

**a)** What water speed is needed to pick up particles of 3 mm diameter?

**b)** At what water speed will particles of 1.5 mm diameter be deposited?

**c)** What does the shaded area represent?

**d)** What is the relationship between the speed of water flow and the size of rock particles carried?

**e)** What range of particle sizes would you expect to be deposited by a river whose water speed suddenly changed from 0.2 m/s to 0.02 m/s?

# A chemist's problem (1)

## Siting a production plant

The development of any new material is carried out only after very thorough research. Unless there is a market for the particular material, then its large-scale production will not be economically viable. The production of any material on a large scale has to be carefully thought out before the production plant is sited. For example, there are different numbers of people seeking employment in different parts of the country. If one of the raw materials has to be shipped in from another country, for example, bauxite for the production of aluminium from countries such as Jamaica, then it may be worth building the production plant near a sea port to reduce transport costs. However, there may be problems recruiting a large enough workforce there.

The manufacture of plastics uses large quantities of ethene and other products from the distillation of crude oil. Most oil refineries are situated near ports with special terminals for the delivery of oil. It may help to have a plastics factory situated nearby to reduce transport costs. This may also help reduce the costs of storing hazardous chemicals, since they can be bought direct and at relatively short notice.

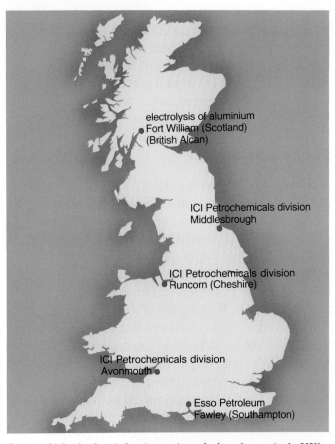

electrolysis of aluminium
Fort William (Scotland)
(British Alcan)

ICI Petrochemicals division
Middlesbrough

ICI Petrochemicals division
Runcorn (Cheshire)

ICI Petrochemicals division
Avonmouth

Esso Petroleum
Fawley (Southampton)

*Can you think why these industries are situated where they are in the UK?*

Another major consideration is the effect on the environment. Recently, more effort has been made to make factories blend in with their environments. Many processes involve problems such as waste gases and the safe disposal of by-products. These have to conform to legislation from the Health and Safety bodies. No one really wants a smelly factory in their back garden! Sometimes things can go tragically wrong, but usually the laws are obeyed and the risk of pollution is reduced. This was not the case during the Industrial Revolution of the 18th century. Little care was taken over the health of the workforce and workers suffered dreadful side effects and even death from their work. Iron works and factories appeared rapidly from 1750 with minimal care for the effects of the environment. In this century the air has often been polluted. It wasn't until after the 'killer fogs' of 1952 and 1956 that a Clean Air Act was passed in Parliament to control the emission of waste gases from factories.

*The industrial pollution that was so prominent during the Industrial Revolution is now a thing of the past. Or is it?*

## Activities

1   Make a plan of the local industries in your area. Think why they are sited where they are and comment on their effect on the environment.

2   Find out about the effects of the Industrial Revolution on the environment and on the people who worked in factories during that time.

3   Find out about the 'killer fog' of 1952.

# A chemist's problem (2)

There have been a number of tragic accidents involving chemicals during the last 20 years. Many of these accidents could have been avoided. The effects of such accidents on the people who live close to the factories and on the environment are too disastrous to put a price on. We need to learn from previous mistakes and try to avoid accidents happening again.

## The Seveso disaster

**Seveso** is a small town in northern Italy. On Saturday 10 July 1976 there was a small explosion in a nearby chemical factory following a chemical reaction that went out of control. A safety valve allowed a cloud of gas to escape. Only 2 kg of gas were released into the atmosphere. Part of the gas was the harmless TCP which is used as an antiseptic. However, it also contained dioxin. Nothing out of the ordinary happened until two weeks later when a farmer found a dead cat. When he picked it up, its tail fell off. More animals were reported dead in neighbouring fields. Shortly after that, people started to experience burns and rashes. The local authorities did not know that the gas that had escaped from the chemical factory contained dioxin until this time. Over 2000 people were evacuated from the town and many were seriously affected by burns. Children were more seriously affected than adults. Many children born after the disaster were seriously deformed.

This accident need not have happened. The people who lived very close to the factory in Seveso were not told of the dangers of dioxin and the people who worked at the factory were oblivious to the problems. The last barrels of chemicals were destroyed there in 1983 and efforts are now being taken to clean the affected area so that people can move back into the town.

*Seveso is still deserted.*

## Oil pollution

Crude oil is a valuable commodity. It is a thick, sticky, dark liquid which is used to make a variety of chemicals. It is transported in enormous tankers, or through long pipes from oil fields. There have been accidents involving the transport of crude oil which could have been avoided. For example, in 1989 the tanker Exxon Valdez lost 11 million gallons of oil which polluted the sea and coast of Alaska causing tremendous environmental problems. It is very difficult to disperse crude oil, but detergents can be used. These detergents also cause damage to the environment. The easiest way to solve these problems is to avoid accidents happening.

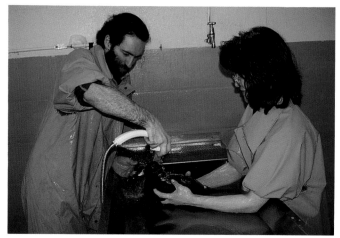

*Birds and animals coated with oil die if they are not cleaned up. The oil also ruins the feeding grounds for many birds.*

## Disposal of toxic chemicals

It is very difficult to dispose of dangerous chemicals safely. Some countries have tighter controls than others on the treatment of toxic waste. Transporting toxic chemicals such as PCBs (polychlorinated biphenyls) can cause more problems than their disposal. The containers chemicals are transported in must be correctly labelled so that they are handled in the safest way possible. People are becoming increasingly more aware of the problems of disposing of this waste, but the amount of toxic waste is increasing.

### Activities

**1**  Collect newspaper articles about problems associated with   **a)** pollution due to chemical factories   **b)** pollution of the sea and coasts by oil and   **c)** the disposal of toxic waste.

# Index